THE PHYSIOLOGICAL BASES
OF MOTIVATION

THE PHYSIOLOGICAL BASES OF MOTIVATION

JACK E. HOKANSON

Florida State University

JOHN WILEY & SONS, INC.

New York London Sydney Toronto

To my wife Cynthia

Preface

Several personal traits are necessary to becoming fascinated by the topic of motivation: (*a*) a kind of tinkerer's delight in gaining an understanding of the way complex machines and physical systems operate; (*b*) a scientist's tolerance of the fact that our data (hence our understanding) are never complete; and (*c*) a philosopher's belief that a grand design in nature awaits our discovery.

This book is an attempt to introduce the student to the physiological bases of motivated behavior. As such, the material is aimed at providing an overview of the experimental and theoretical developments in the field rather than a detailed account of the myriad studies that have been carried out. Within this framework many specific issues concerning technological and research problems have been omitted, and the reader is cautioned against easy generalizations. In addition, when dealing with the physiological aspects of behavior, we inevitably become involved in anatomical detail. The reader may therefore find it helpful to begin this book by reading the appendix on the nervous system or by using a textbook on physiological psychology, such as Grossman's work (1967) as a general reference.

Aside from the inherently interesting nature of motivated phenomena, it is hoped that the reader will gain an appreciation of another aspect of the field, namely, the communal nature of these investigations. Perhaps more so than any other subfield in the behavioral sciences, physiologically oriented researchers seem to work as a community of scientists—spending time in one another's laboratory, collaborating on common experimental problems, and teaching one another. It may well be that the very complexity of the phenomena under study and the technical skills required have forced this kind of collaborated effort.

The reader should recognize that research on the physiology of motivation is in an early stage of development. New perspectives are being opened up at an amazing rate, so that we find ourselves continually on the threshold of some new insights into the fundamental nature of behavior.

I wish to thank several people for their invaluable assistance in the preparation of this book: Drs. D. R. Kenshalo and Douglas Grimsley for their many helpful suggestions and discussions, Karl R. Willers and Judith Seymour for their work in preparing the figures and graphs, and, finally, Lynda Stringer, Victoria Stoner, and Robyn Talley for converting my illegible handwriting into a typed manuscript.

Tallahassee, 1969   *Jack E. Hokanson*

Contents

I

Approaches to the Study
of Motivation

Let us begin with an assumption: all behavior is causally determined. In our scientific and mechanistic culture, this is no longer considered an extreme point of view; moreover, most current-day behavioral scientists are proponents of this deterministic thesis. In many ways our everyday curiosities reflect the same philosophy because we frequently ask such questions as, Why did he do that? or, I wonder why I reacted that way? Answering the question "why" with respect to behavior is the subject matter of the topic of motivation.

In spite of this basic philosophical agreement, psychologists have differed as to which is the appropriate level of study. Physiologically oriented psychologists such as Hebb (1951) have been primarily concerned with an investigation of how bodily processes are related (or covary) with behavior. This approach focuses on the neural and biochemical determinants of an organism's responses. At the other extreme have been psychologists who felt that the proper concern of the field should be the finding of lawful stimulus-response relationships (behavioral principles) while leaving the internal, physiological workings of the body to other disciplines (e.g., Skinner, 1953). The focus here has, therefore, been largely on the reinforcements, punishments, deprivations, and other conditions imposed by the environment and how these stimuli govern behavior.

In recent years there has been a growing recognition that neither camp can provide a complete understanding of behavior. For example, a body of research is developing which indicates that appropriately programmed external stimuli can significantly alter physiological events according to learning principles (Razran, 1961). Thus an understanding of the physiological events alone, without consideration of the environmental stimuli involved, would provide an incomplete picture of behavior. Similarly, a

1

study of the sexual behavior of infrahuman organisms, for example, exclusively in terms of environmental stimuli would leave the scientist woefully uninformed about the very complex hormonal and neural influences on this behavior. In short then, an adequate investigation of behavior requires study at both levels of inquiry, with an appreciation of how physiological processes and environmental contingencies interact to produce complex patterns of response.

Within the field of psychology there have been a limited number of topics which have lent themselves to this dual type of analysis. These are the areas of general arousal, hunger, thirst, temperature regulation, sexual and parental behavior, responses to pain, and the concept of reinforcement. As such they have become grouped together under the general topic of *motivation*. The aim of this book is to review the theories and experimental work pertaining to these topics. Emphasis will be placed on the physiological determinants of the behaviors involved, but with an attempt to include the important environmental and learning factors as well.

POINTS OF VIEW

Attempts to explain the behavior of man and animals probably date to the development of mankind. Any detailed account of the history of these philosophical and scientific points of view is well beyond the scope of this chapter; however, a review of the main threads of argument should provide some perspective on the later material in this book.

The predominant view of motivation in Western culture from the time of the ancient Greeks to the seventeenth century emphasized man's free will and his ability to exercise rationality. With the use of his reason man could evaluate alternative courses of action and make free and rational choices. In the same vein, brutish passions and desires could be controlled by his ability to reason. This Greek rationalistic philosophy (Socrates, Plato, and Aristotle) endured and gained a degree of universality in Christian theology as reflected in the writings of St. Augustine and St. Thomas Aquinas, wherein the ethical-moral aspects of correct behavior and control of instincts gained ascendence. Man was thus held accountable for his choices of action—a view obviously predominant in current-day legal-philosophic traditions as well.

With the rise of physical sciences in the seventeenth and eighteenth centuries more mechanistic views of motivation emerged. Physical events could be explained on the basis of mechanical principles, as could the behavior of organisms. For Descartes (1596–1650) animals, lacking the rationality of man, behaved automatically on the basis of internal or external forces; whereas for man, possessing reason, behavior was the resultant of a complex interaction between bodily conditions and the exercise of rationality. More uncompromising was Thomas Hobbes (1588–1679), who held that all behaviors could be accounted for on the basis of physical motions. In addition, Hobbes maintained essentially a hedonistic position in which man was viewed as being motivated by the pursuit of pleasure and avoidance of pain—a philosophical orientation which, of course, ran counter to the free-will viewpoint. This mechanistic-hedonistic philosophy also had its roots in Greek antiquity (Democritus and Epicurus), but did not really come to fruition until the intellectual revolution following the Middle Ages.

Embedded in most of the motivational theories up until the seventeenth century were concerns about two major issues: the morality of mans' behavior and an uncovering of the divine plan of nature. With the rise of mechanistic views of the world and subsequent growth of physiological research in the eighteenth and nineteenth centuries, these scholastic issues began to recede. The culmination of this historical development was the work of Charles Darwin (1859) in which neither the ethics of behavior nor the possibility of divine intervention was considered. Life was viewed as involving continual competition and struggle for existing food, space, etc., in which organisms with the most appropriate adaptive equipment survived. This "survival of the fittest" notion evidently grew out of Darwin's observations of animal behavior during his world travels and the earlier work of Malthus concerning the growth of population and limited supplies of life's necessities. The survivors then, having increased opportunities for procreation, produce offspring which likely possess the adaptive characteristics also. By this process of "natural selection," behavioral and physical attributes evolve over generations in interaction with particular environmental pressures to which the species is subjected. Here then was a theory of nature which did not rely on a deistic plan, nor was it one in which man was given any privileged position. The unfolding of nature (including man) was accounted for by the postulation of some initial differences among organisms followed by the ever-present process of natural selection.

Central to Darwin's view of behavior was the notion of instincts, which were considered as automatic, innately determined behaviors on the part of the organism to internal or external stimuli. Although implicit in many earlier views of behavior, the placing of this concept in an evolutionary framework gave great impetus to naturalistic studies of animals and to later attempts to investigate the biological bases for instinctual behaviors.

A significant convergence of Darwinian theory and the hedonistic viewpoint occurred in the work of Herbert Spencer (1862). He argued that

behaviors which produce pleasure are also those which are likely to promote survival; similarly, behaviors which result in pain probably signal
that survival is threatened. From an evolutionary viewpoint, this correlation between pleasure and survival (pain and threatened survival)
seemed to Spencer to be eminently adaptive for the organism. Moreover,
Spencer gave a new emphasis to the pleasure-pain viewpoint by focusing
on the learning of behaviors on the basis of pleasurable or aversive outcomes. Thus responses are not emitted because of some future goal, but
on the basis of the organism's past history of reinforcements—a viewpoint
remarkably similar to current-day operant conditioning theory.

With the theoretical contributions of Darwin and Spencer man's concept of himself received profound blows. No longer was he placed in a
unique, theologically ordained category in the universe; man was simply
another, though highly adaptive and evolved, organism in the natural
order of the world. In addition, the freedom-of-choice concept gave way
to the new hedonism of Spencer, wherein past events in a person's life
programmed behavior. Following shortly after these developments yet
another blow to man's philosophical views of himself occurred in the
contributions of Freud (1915). Here man was viewed as not only being
driven by instinctual urges but many of these processes were considered
to be outside of awareness. The destruction of the concept of man as a
rational, conscious, decision-making being was now virtually complete.

By passing over the many currents and eddies of controversy that took
place in the nineteenth century, we see that early twentieth-century
motivational theory developed with several emphases: (a) the role of
instincts as inborn, biologically determined energizers of behavior; (b)
the effects of pleasure and pain in the learning of behaviors; and (c) a
committment to a scientific method of investigation. Continuing into more
recent times, these traditions have evolved along several lines, perhaps
most easily dichotomized into what can be called an *empiricist approach*
and a *biological approach*.

The empiricist tradition, in a large sense growing out of nineteenth-
century physics, was a reaction against a strict mechanistic viewpoint.
Theorists in the empiricist mould maintained that the aim of a science was
to describe lawful relationships between variables in as precise a fashion
as possible. The constructs in a theory could be viewed as just constructs
and nothing else, and did not necessarily have to refer to some underlying
mechanical process. Within the field of psychology this tradition seemed
to merge with another, older, philosophical viewpoint concerning motivation—the hedonistic orientation—to produce strong interest in the question of the variables affecting learning. Theorists such as E. L. Thorndike
(1874–1949) and J. B. Watson (1919), following in the tradition of
Spencer, did extensive experimental work on the effects of rewards and

punishments in learning and behavioral acquisition. In addition, Watson reacted against the earlier instinct models of behavior, and emphasized the flexibility and modifiability of behavior. This new "behaviorism" quite ardently attempted to exclude what were felt to be pseudoexplanatory concepts, such as instinct, in favor of a strictly empirical analysis of observable stimulus and response variables.

In terms of motivational theory then, the rise of an empirical, behavioral approach during the 1920s and 1930s was associated with a concomitant decline of explanations of behavior based on instinctual processes or anticipations (conscious states) of future pleasure or pain. Rather, the control of behavior was viewed as a function of the organism's past history of rewards and punishments and aspects of the current stimulus situation. Interestingly enough, however, the notion that the biological status of the organism played an important role in behavior did not remain submerged. A construct which made reference to forces which impelled behavior was needed. The concept of *drive* was first introduced by Woodworth (1918) and, after some definitional disagreements within the field, achieved a major place in a unified theory of behavior proposed by Clark Hull (1943).

Hull's concept of drive does not permit easy definition, since it was a construct with referents in several directions—to antecedent events, to overt responses, to presumed bodily conditions, and to another construct, habit strength. Drive, as a concept in Hull's theory, was viewed as basically being a function of physiological need, and in most of Hull's laboratory work this was experimentally defined by the length of time that the organism had been deprived of food. This deprivation state (and associated bodily need) was considered to give rise to characteristic internal stimuli, which could then function just as other stimuli in becoming associated with particular responses. It should be noted, then, that the motivational construct of drive was ultimately tied to biological needs of the organism, although in Hull's work the concern was not with identifying the actual physiological structures or processes involved in bodily depletion.

On the response side, drive was considered to have primarily an energizing effect on behavior, as could be noted in increased vigor or speed of responding and greater probabilities of making certain consummatory behaviors. In this same context, Hull attempted to provide a more direct definition for the concept of reinforcement (the more modern derivative of the pleasure concept from hedonistic theory) in which a *reduction in drive* was seen as the underlying mechanism of reinforcement. Since drive level and the actual tissue needs typically covary together, the reinforcement construct also was given an ultimate physiological referent.

The strength of stimulus-response associations (habit strength) in

Hullian theory was viewed as a function of (among other factors) reinforcement history. In an over-all sense, then, Hull attempted to relate overt, observable behaviors to the current status of drive (energizing or motivating behavior) and habit strength (providing the direction of behavior on the basis of past history). Within the empiricist tradition, Hull's contribution represents a very elegant attempt to develop a theory of behavior, by using both motivational and associative constructs, but without specifying (except in a most general sense) the actual physiological mechanics underlying the constructs. By postulating a multiplicative interaction between drive and habit strength, Hull's model was able to account for a great deal of the behavior of laboratory animals in learning experiments. As we shall see in Chapter VIII however, Hull's concepts of reinforcement and drive reduction have led to a vast array of subsequent research attempting to clarify the physiology underlying these constructs.

Turning to the more directly biological tradition in motivational research in the twentieth century, we see a somewhat different set of emphases from that of the empiricists. Several lines of development are apparent, all in some way concerned with elucidating the physiological processes which underlie behavior or perception. Perhaps a fundamental tradition within experimental psychology was a concern about sensory processes and nervous transmission from the receptor to the brain. In terms of modern developments in this area we can mention one of the giants of the nineteenth century, Hermann Helmholtz (1821–1894). His greatest contributions were in the area of the physiology of vision and audition; his published texts in both subjects are still classics today. His theories of color vision, of specific nerve fiber energies (by which to account for different sensory qualities), and the resonance theory of hearing are perhaps his best-known contributions, although his work in sensory psychology was far more encyclopedic than implied by these references. Experimental work attempting to describe the physical processes in the chain of events from sensory stimulation to perception has continued as a strong tradition, with the work of Adrian on the refractory period and the all-or-none principle of nerve transmission (Adrian, 1914), and, later, Troland in vision and von Bekesy in audition representing some of the major contributors during the 1920s and 1930s.

Parallel developments during the nineteenth and early twentieth centuries were taking place in attempts to describe the neurology underlying various types of behaviors. During the 1860s Broca was able to localize the speech center in the brain, and shortly thereafter Fritsch and Hitzig described the motor area in the precentral cortex. Ferrier and Munk, working during the 1870s and 1880s, elucidated the visual functions of the occipital lobe. Shortly after the turn of the century, Sherrington made his monumental contributions concerning the physiology of the reflex and the coordination of reflexes in complex behaviors. Franz at about the same time and, later on, Lashley, worked on the functions of the cerebrum in habit formation and retention. During the 1920s and 1930s Cannon made his major contributions concerning the role of the sympathetic nervous system and hypothalamus in emotions, and the physiology of hunger and thirst. Finally the work of Pavlov on conditioned reflexes during the first decades of the twentieth century, particularly those concerned with the digestive system, represents an important meeting ground of physiological and learning variables.

A third line of development, growing largely out of Darwin's contributions, was that of comparative psychology—cross-species studies of animal behavior. Perhaps the most significant post-Darwinian development was the rise of experimental laboratories of animal behavior in the United States at the turn of the century by such figures as Thorndike and Yerkes, wherein aspects of "animal intelligence" (sensory discrimination, learning, problem solving, etc.) could be studied under controlled conditions. Loeb, during this same period, had an important impact on American psychology in proposing a strongly mechanistic view of animal behavior. These traditions of comparative study continued in the next several decades through the work of such figures as Hunter, dealing with complex discrimination processes, and Köhler, from a different vantage point, studying perception and problem solving. More recently, a concern with instinctive behavior has been rearoused through the work of such ethologists as Lorenz (e.g., 1939) and Tinbergen (1951), wherein the emphasis has been on innate behavior patterns and the environmental conditions which elicit them.

We can see, then, a multiplicity of approaches to gaining understanding of behavior. On one hand, the level of theorizing has become more precise, deterministic, and empirically based over the years. At the same time, technological advances have permitted more controlled and subtle experimental approaches to these problems in the laboratory. In the next section of this chapter, a brief review of the major methodological approaches within the area of the physiological study of motivation will be covered. It is hoped that the current sections on the history and technical developments concerning the study of motivation will serve as an adequate entrée into the topics to be covered in subsequent chapters.

METHODS OF PHYSIOLOGICAL RESEARCH

The experimental study of the physical systems of the body has gone through some fascinating developments, largely produced by such technological advances as electronic amplifiers, cathode-ray oscilloscopes, and, most recently, computers. In this section, the major laboratory approaches to the nervous system are reviewed, leaving some of the subsidiary techniques to be covered in the appropriate, later chapters. For the present, the following basic procedures are mentioned: neuroanatomical methods; the production of lesions; electrical recording techniques; and brain stimulation approaches.

Neuroanatomical Methods

The neuroanatomical approach refers to the dissection and visual study of the nervous system. It ranges from the mere identification of the major structures and nerve tracts of the brain to the microscopic study of single nerve fibers and cell bodies. The study of gross anatomy has been important in making comparisons across different species concerning the development of various brain structures. More important in recent years, however, has been the microscopic study of neural elements, thus allowing detailed investigations concerning (a) the tracing of the routes of single nerve fibers; (b) the molecular composition of nerve cells; (c) the structural properties of synapses; and (d) with the electron microscope, the study of such subcellular structures as nerve membranes. All, of course, relate to the study of the fundamental nature of information transmission in neural fibers.

The microscopic study of the nervous system requires the use of fixatives and staining techniques. Fixatives are substances which prevent the decay of the organic matter being studied. Stains are chemicals which selectively dye the particular neural element (e.g., cell body or nerve fiber) to be viewed under the microscope. In rough outline, the preparation to be investigated goes through the following steps: (a) introducing the fixative into the body usually through a main artery immediately after the death of the organism; (b) hardening the neural material (in wax or by freezing) in preparation for cutting very thin sections of the tissue; (c) mounting the sections on slides and staining.

Brain Lesions

There are two main experimental uses for the surgical destruction of nervous system tissue: the tracing of nerve fibers and, more important for our purposes, the evaluation of behavioral effects. With respect to the former, fiber tracts or nuclei can be destroyed, and the resulting degenerative process in the neural subsystem can provide a picture (via appropriate staining techniques) of the circuitry involved. This, of course, is an important technique in studying the origins and terminations of fiber tracts in the immensely complex tangle of neurons in the brain.

Of greater psychological importance, however, are the studies which attempt to assess the behavioral effects of brain lesions. Here an attempt is made to determine which brain structures subserve specific behaviors. These procedures require the consideration of several methodological issues: (a) precise and reliable measurement of the behavior under question before and after the production of the lesion; (b) ensurance that only the selected brain region has been destroyed so that the behavioral changes cannot be attributed to other physical defects (e.g., destruction of adjacent structures); (c) verification by later neuroanatomical study that the selected site for the lesion was in fact destroyed; (d) the use of control lesions at other sites to determine the specific effects of the lesioned area; and (e) the use of appropriate surgical techniques so that behavioral changes cannot be attributed to such factors as postoperative infections.

Of great importance in studies using brain lesions was the development of the *stereotaxic instrument*. This is a precisely constructed frame which, in effect, holds the experimental organism's head in a fixed position in all three planes. The instrument has graduated scales in all planes so that any point within the skull can be exactly fixed by three coordinates. The frame, of course, is so constructed that electrodes or surgical probes can be mounted and inserted into the brain with reasonable precision.

Electrical Recording

The recording of electrical activity in the nervous system usually involves a three-component apparatus: electrodes to pick up the bioelectric signals; an amplification system which reliably magnifies these potentials; and a read-out component which provides a permanent record of the data. In general, there are also three levels of measurement discernible in recording techniques in current use: gross surface recordings; electrodes placed in groups of nerve cells (e.g., a nucleus of the hypothalamus); and microelectrode recording from a single nerve cell body. Selection of the appropriate recording setup depends, of course, on the nature of the experiment being conducted.

Surface recordings, usually via disk electrodes pasted on the subject's scalp, produce data reflecting the general electric-potential variations in different portions of the cortex. These electroencephalographic (EEG) signals are fed into an amplification system and then translated into mechanical movements of a pen. A permanent record of the brain activity is thereby produced on a strip of paper moving at a constant speed underneath the pen. Changes in the frequency, amplitude, and regularity (synchrony) of these EEG records are the primary data gathered in studies ranging from the cortical effects of visual stimulation to changes occurring during sleep and various levels of arousal (see Chapter II).

The use of electrodes implanted into the brain requires several additional procedures. While the subject is under anesthesia, the electrodes are inserted through a small burr hole in the skull with the use of a stereotaxic instrument. The electrodes usually consist of finely drawn stainless-steel wires (varying in size depending on the area to be studied) that are insulated except for the small exposed tip. The leads are cemented to the burr hole and terminate in a socket. This produces a permanently implanted unit, and when an investigator wants to record electrical activity in the awake animal, he merely has to "plug" the subject into the amplification and read-out system. In more recent developments the electrodes terminate in a miniaturized radio transmitter, the signals from which are picked up by a radio receiver some distance away. The output of the receiver is then fed into the usual amplification systems. This telemetry technique has the great advantage of not requiring constraining wires attached to the subject's skull, thus allowing for greater flexibility of movement during recording. Permanent records of the data can again be obtained with ink-writing pen units, or the potential changes can be fed into a cathode-ray oscilloscope, and then, in turn, be photographed.

Another recent development is the use of computers in analyzing the complex output of the recording system. In almost any bioelectric system there is a certain degree of "noise" which tends to mask the electrical activity under investigation. Computers attached directly to the output of the amplification system can be programmed to "average out" the undesirable noise, analyze complex waveforms, and perform other laborious computations on the data.

Stimulation Techniques

Much the same basic procedures as previously outlined in implanting electrodes are performed in electrically stimulating areas of the brain. As a matter of fact, in current usage, the permanently implanted units have multiple wires enabling the investigator to both record and stimulate— again by remote control if desired. Of added interest has been the development of electronic stimulators with which the investigator can very precisely control the intensity, duration, and waveform of the stimulating current.

Finally, mention should be made of techniques by which the brain can be chemically or thermally stimulated. In the former procedure a very fine piece of tubing is inserted into the brain (much the same as an electrode) and chemical agents can be introduced through this *cannula*. With thermal stimulation a finely drawn loop can be inserted into areas of the brain through which water is passed at predetermined temperatures.

Summary

These brief outlines of experimental techniques should provide the reader with a general background to pursue the content of subsequent chapters. Obviously, considerable detail has been omitted but, when necessary, these specifics will be discussed as part of the particular topics later in the book. Finally, it is hoped that the student has gained some appreciation of the many technical skills required before adequate research can be done in the area of motivation.

PLAN OF THIS BOOK

A strictly empirical philosophy is a tough one to live by, particularly when writing a book. In the absence of an organizing theory, research evidence tends to become compartmentalized and unrelated to other evidence, with the result that the reader does not gain a reasonable overview of a topic. Nevertheless it is felt that superficial theorizing does not perform any service for the serious student of behavior. Hence the aim of this book is to acquaint the reader with the main lines of research evidence in the area of motivation. It is hoped that frequent summaries and reviews will gradually provide a cohesive picture of the complex behaviors to be covered—as far as our current knowledge will allow. Needless to say, there will be many gaps in our understanding because there is still much to be learned in the area.

In rough outline the chapters will proceed as follows: Chapters II through VIII will cover arousal, hunger, thirst, temperature regulation, sex, pain-motivated behavior, and the physiology of reinforcement, respectively. With each new topic an attempt is made to review first the known behavioral facts about the area, to be followed by a more detailed treatment of the physiological systems which control the behavior. Lastly, where possible, the relationship between physiological and environmental controls will be highlighted.

II

The Concept of Physiological Arousal

As we shall see in succeeding chapters, the physiological processes involved in hunger, thirst, temperature regulation, and sex exhibit a remarkable patterning and sequencing. Neural, biochemical, and behavioral events are tied together in complex interactions that undoubtedly rival the most advanced computers of today. Before getting to these intricate topics however, it will be necessary to review a more basic dimension of physiological activity—that of arousal. Although this is a more general way of viewing the biology of motivational phenomena, the topic nevertheless has a long history and still is a central issue in the field today.

The term *level of arousal* has been used essentially to describe, in an over-all way, the degree of biological activity manifested by an organism at any particular moment. At the simplest level it has been viewed as a continuum—with deep sleep at one extreme and intense excitement at the other. There would be an infinity of intermediate states, some of which might be described by such terms as drowsy, relaxed, calm, alert, tense, etc. (Bindra, 1959). Hence it is a concept which attempts to order the intensive aspects of an organism's functioning.

The intensity dimension has been an important part of psychological theories for at least 60 years. Wundt (1897), in his early conception of emotions, suggested that intensity was one of the basic dimensions involved. Cannon's *emergency theory* of emotions in 1929 and the work of Elizabeth Duffy (1941) emphasized the *energy mobilization* that takes place during states of strong emotion. More recently, Moruzzi and Magoun (1949) have approached the arousal concept from a directly physiological point of view, having succeeded in isolating some of the anatomical structures that underlie the sleep—excitement continuum. Lindsley (1951) subsequently incorporated these findings in his *activation theory of emotions*.

12

Aside from physiologists concerned with the topic of emotions, many learning theorists have also displayed an interest in the intensive aspects of behavior. Thus, for example, such a concept as *generalized drive* was a central part of Hull's (1943) very influential learning theory. Although Hull and some of his followers (Hilgard, 1956) used this drive notion in a purely hypothetical way to describe certain deprivation states (with no reference to actual bodily processes), it frequently was used to explain motivated behavior. Regardless of the logical difficulties inherent in such usage (Malmo, 1958), the fact remains that some of the major learning theorists of the past several decades have recognized the importance of this basic dimension.

In the realm of clinical psychology and personality theory, the arousal dimension has also found a place. Freudian and neo-Freudian theories of personality particularly invoke such concepts as *psychic energy, tension,* and *anxiety* to describe the subjective states induced by stress or biological needs. An extension of this line of thinking has been the attempt by Spence (1958) to treat the clinical concept of anxiety as an important factor in his learning theory construct of *generalized drive.*

We see then that the arousal concept has had an appeal throughout the history of psychology; and it still represents a major tenet in a diversity of areas within the field today. In most instances, however, theorists have used it in a vague way to refer to the energy manifested in the sum total of physiological processes, thus recognizing the importance of biological variables in the understanding of behavior but, at the same time, neglecting to study the specifics of the physiology involved. The pioneer work started by Moruzzi and Magoun in 1949 and Lindsley in 1951, in which they outline an anatomical basis for the arousal dimension, represents then a major breakthrough in the study of the concept. Now, it has become possible to measure and/or manipulate the actual physical events associated with various levels of arousal—a procedure far better suited to provide an empirical basis for the concept.

In this chapter we shall review the physiology underlying the concept and summarize the relationship between these physiological events and overt behavior.

THE PHYSIOLOGY OF AROUSAL

There are three principle structures in the brain which have been implicated in the sleep-excitement dimension. These are the cortex, the hypothalamus, and the reticular formation. Each area will be reviewed separately, followed by an attempt to provide an integration of the arousal process.

Cortical Processes

The most frequently used device to measure the electrical activity in the brain is the electroencephalograph (EEG). Surface electrodes can be pasted on the scalp of the subject or, in some instances, needle electrodes are implanted in the brain, which detect changes in electric potential. The potential changes that are picked up by these electrodes are fed into an amplification system and then translated into pen deflections on a moving strip of recording paper or placed on magnetic tape. In this way, the frequency, amplitude, and other characteristics of the electrical changes can be studied in detail.

Visual inspection and scoring of EEG records have proved to be extremely tedious and inexact procedures. More recent approaches involve recording on magnetic tape, which can then be processed through a computer. The counting of waves per unit of time or the occurrences of various wave frequencies can then be carried out by the computer, thus providing a picture of much more subtle changes in brain activity which might be lost to mere hand scoring of the record. In this fashion, frequency and power distributions as well as phase analyses can be obtained which show in detail the shifts in the brain's activity under a variety of experimental conditions.

It appears that with scalp electrodes the EEG provides a picture of the changes in potential in large numbers of cells of the cortex. To be sure, these cortical potentials are influenced by neural events deeper within the brain. When masses of cells are changing polarity together, a relatively regular, synchronous EEG pattern is obtained—a pattern characteristic of relaxation or deep sleep. During periods of alertness or activity, the cortical rhythms are typically desynchronized, most likely influenced by altered processes in the brain-stem reticular formation (see below). These desynchronous patterns are also characteristic of certain aspects of sleep, notably times when the organism appears to be dreaming.

With respect to the present topic, the EEG has provided some of the basic data. The frequency, amplitude, and other characteristics of cortical activity have been found to vary according to the degree of behavioral arousal displayed by the subject (Jasper, 1958). Figure 2.1 shows typical human EEG records during a variety of these conditions. Note the pattern on the second record from the top. During a period of relaxation, the pattern is regular (synchronous), the waves are of moderate amplitude (voltage), and their frequency is about 10 to 14 per second. These are the rather well-known alpha waves that occur during states of waking restfulness. This pattern represents a convenient base from which to compare cortical changes that take place when arousal conditions are altered in

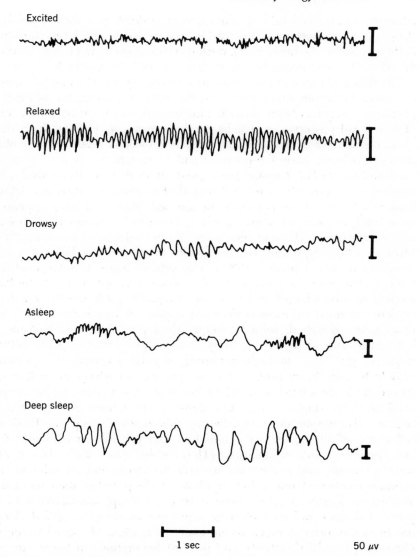

Figure 2.1 Various human EEG patterns under several arousal states. [From H. Jasper, in Penfield and Erickson, *Epilepsy and Cerebral Localization*. Springfield, Ill.: Charles C. Thomas, 1941, p. 212. (*Courtesy of Charles C. Thomas, publisher.*)]

either direction. As a subject drifts into drowsiness and various levels of sleep, the alpha pattern is replaced by the much slower, large-amplitude *delta* waves. On the other hand, during states of excitement (top record), the waves become desynchronized, fast, and of low amplitude.

The depth of human sleep seems to vary throughout the night's sojourn, one level fusing imperceptibly with the next. However, for descriptive purposes, sleep has been divided into several stages, using EEG, other physiological processes, and behavioral responses as criteria. In a stage generally termed *drowsiness*, the human subject is relatively immobile, with eyes closed. Body temperature and heart rate are beginning to decline and the EEG is forming the regular alpha rhythm. Subjectively, this appears to be typically a relaxed period of random thoughts and images from which the subject can easily be aroused. Stage 1 of sleep appears to be a brief, transitional phase in which the EEG becomes more uneven and desynchronized, with generally lower voltages (Kamiya, 1961). Muscles relax, respiration becomes more even, and the heart rate continues to decline (Snyder, 1960). The subject again can be awakened with relative ease. As a deeper level of sleep develops, stage 2, the EEG amplitude grows larger and there are frequent quick bursts of activity evident. Minimal stimulation does not appear to arouse the subject but, upon being wakened, subjects frequently report that they had merely been in a state of reverie. In stage 3 the rapid bursts of EEG activity begin to give way to high-amplitude, regular patterns. Temperature, muscle tension, heart rate, and blood pressure continue to decline and considerable stimulation is required to awaken the subject. In the deepest level of sleep, stage 4, the EEG shows a continuous pattern of slow, regular, high-amplitude waves. During this depth of sleep, the EEG will reflect the effects of sensory stimulation, but the subject evidently does not "perceive" this stimulation (Hernandez-Peon, 1963). Heart rate, muscle tension, and respiration are still declining, and stimulation may produce movement into a lighter phase of sleep rather than immediate awakening. Lastly, a rather unique stage of sleep, associated with reports of dreams and characteristic rapid eye movements (REM sleep), has been the focus of much recent experimentation. Heralded by desynchronized, fast EEG activity and marked fluctuations in heart rate and other autonomic processes (Snyder, 1963), the subject appears to be undergoing some form of arousal, even though he is, by any usual definition, still asleep. This area of dream research will be dealt with more specifically at the end of this chapter.

The other end of the arousal continuum has been termed by Lindsley (1951) an *activation pattern* and is produced, in varying degrees, by sensory stimulation, muscular exertion, intellectual work, or emotional experiences. At its most general level, then, it reflects the cortical state of affairs when the organism is undergoing some interchange with the environment or is actively engaged in internal, symbolic activity.

It is now clear that these cortical electrical phenomena are markedly dependent on neural events that occur in lower centers in the brain—notably in certain portions of the hypothalamus and the reticular formation. As we shall see, these structures along with the cortex interact with each other and also with several other major physiological systems—the sensory, the endocrine, the somatic (musculature), and the autonomic nervous systems. We have here then, a broad involvement of most of the important aspects of the organism's physiology, all in some way playing a role in determining over-all "arousal."

Hypothalamus

In later chapters, the very important functions of the hypothalamus concerning hunger, thirst, temperature, sex, and emotions will be reviewed. In this section, however, we review only those portions of this structure involving the sleep-excitement continuum; see Figure A.3.

Most important here is the posterior area, a portion of the hypothalamus critical for maintaining wakefulness. Lesions in this area produce lasting sleep and drowsiness (Ranson, 1939). Although strong sensory stimulation can temporarily awaken the subject, he immediately returns to somnolence upon termination of the stimulus. On the other hand, in an intact organism, electrical stimulation of appropriate intensity applied to the posterior hypothalamus produces waking alertness and excitement (Hess, 1954).

It is interesting to note that this posterior area also exerts a major degree of control on sympathetic, autonomic activity. Aside from eliciting wakefulness, electrical stimulation at this site produces the whole array of autonomic responses usually associated with *energy mobilization*, e.g., increases in heart rate, blood pressure, blood sugar level, vasoconstriction, muscle tension, respiration rate, etc. Furthermore, the secretion of epinephrine by the adrenal medulla also is under sympathetic control, and thus can be traced back ultimately to posterior hypothalamic influences. In this context, the term *arousal* takes on more concrete meaning, involving not only cortical changes but also a more general alteration in patterns of activity throughout the body.

To continue this discussion of the hypothalamus, mention should be made of the anterior area as well. This region seems to play a generally antagonistic role with respect to the posterior effects. Associated with control of the parasympathetic division of the autonomic nervous system, electrical stimulation of the anterior hypothalamus brings about *decreases* in blood pressure, blood sugar level, and so on, thus having effects which run counter to posterior stimulation. Lesions in the anterior area, on the other hand, produce organisms which may be chronically aroused, very likely because the restraining influences on the posterior hypothalamus have been removed.

Lastly, the hypothalamic control of the pituitary gland has important ramifications for understanding the biochemical component of arousal. As will be seen in subsequent chapters, the pituitary, via its trophic hormones, governs the hormonal secretions of other important endocrine glands. Thyroxin from the thyroid, a primary chemical agent in the regulation of metabolism rate, is one important system under pituitary control. Steroids secreted by the adrenal cortex and sexual hormones from the gonads are likewise directly regulated by pituitary hormones. All of these substances have rather striking effects in enhancing the over-all vigor and general level of activity of the organism, thus emphasizing their role in affecting the sleep-excitement dimension of behavior.

We see, therefore, that the hypothalamus is a central structure with respect to physical activity in that it is the site of convergence of many diverse systems—the autonomic, hormonal, skeletomuscular, and the internal organs. Little wonder, then, that lesions in critical areas of this structure can have such profound effects on behavior. One last point of overlap is of particular interest: the posterior hypothalamus is anatomically the upper part of the brain-stem reticular formation (BSRF) (Scheibel and Scheibel, 1958).

Reticular Formation

Of all the structures in the central nervous system, the reticular formation has probably received the widest attention with respect to arousal research. Anatomically this system extends from the medulla through the posterior hypothalamus up to the lower thalamus. It consists of a dense and complex network of interconnected neurons which seem to function in a relatively diffuse manner.

The relationship of the reticular formation to other systems is of particular interest. The major afferent pathways from the musculature and viscera of the body have inputs into the BSRF. Thus activity in the musculature or internal organs produce heightened electric discharge in this region. Similarly, the visual, auditory, and other sensory systems send important collateral nerve fibers to the reticular formation so that, again, sensory stimulation produces associated reticular activity. We see then that virtually any stimulation of the organism, be it from external or internal sources, is associated with a general arousal of the BSRF.

Of equal importance are the diffuse projections from the reticular formation to the cortex. Although the routes have not been clearly demarcated, it appears that these fiber systems extend from the upper portion of the reticular formation to all the major areas of the cortex. Thus electrical activity in the reticular formation has the resultant effect of arousing the cortex generally. Finding this reticular-cortical relationship was indeed the first major research breakthrough with respect to the arousal topic. Moruzzi and Magoun in 1949 demonstrated that electrical stimulation of the BSRF produced an activation pattern on the cortical EEG record. Thus, for example, with a relaxed organism the characteristic alpha EEG pattern could be observed; however, upon reticular stimulation, a desynchronous, high-frequency low-voltage excitement record was produced. Complementary findings were obtained by Lindsley et al. (1950) in which lesions were made in the reticular formation. Under these conditions the animals appeared behaviorally to go to sleep and, of course, their EEG records showed typical sleep patterns.

With this brief review of the BSRF the physiology underlying the sleep-excitement dimension comes into clearer focus. In a situation where the organism assumes a relaxed posture, there is a reduced input, via the somatic sensory systems, into the reticular formation. Add to this a diminution of visual and other sensory stimulations which further reduces reticular activity. This relatively reduced level of neural activity in the BSRF is, in turn, reflected in the development of more regular, high-amplitude EEG potentials—and we have some of the important physiological, behavioral, and environmental conditions necessary for drowsiness and sleep. On the other hand, with strong and varied sensory stimulation and postural adjustments involving muscular tension, visceral activity, etc., there are relatively intense and multiple inputs into the reticular formation which, in turn, produce cortical activation patterns. The over-all intensity of this input could be conceived of as determining, in large measure, the subjective sensation of arousal.

To complete this picture of the BSRF, several other relationships need to be mentioned. In addition to the input from the musculature and viscera already reviewed, the reticular formation also sends efferent fibers back to the skeletomuscular system, thus being capable of influencing these bodily systems in a reciprocal fashion. Likewise, there is evidence (French et al., 1955) that the cortex also sends fibers to the reticular formation. Hence cortical events are capable of arousing the BSRF as well as vice versa. Lastly, it has been demonstrated that there are cells in the reticular formation which are sensitive to epinephrine (Jasper, 1958). Therefore the secretion of this arousing hormone by the adrenal medulla (which, it will be recalled, is regulated by sympathetic discharge) has a return effect on the central nervous system in that it produces heightened activity in the BSRF.

Despite many confirming studies following the Lindsley work in 1950, the conclusion that arousal is solely dependent on the reticular formation must, however, be tempered by results of several more recent studies. These investigations found that, when care was taken to avoid surgical shock, by producing lesions in the reticular formation in successive, small steps, the EEG and behavioral signs of arousal were not abolished (Ademetz, 1959; Chow et al., 1959). The implications of these findings are that other regions of the brain also mediate cortical arousal. Work by Green and Arduini (1954) and Grastyan et al. (1959), for example, point to the hippocampus as a likely area for limbic system influences on the arousal response. Furthermore, Eidelberg et al. (1959) implicated the septal region and midline nuclei in the thalamus as being involved in the hippocampal-cortical arousal process. Kaada and Johannessen (1960) have demonstrated that behavioral and EEG arousal patterns are produced by electrical stimulation to a variety of points in the hippocampus and medial cortex. Lastly, there are nuclei at the level of the thalamus which appear to be nonspecific in their projections to the cortex. This system has been also implicated in the arousal response and very likely mediates briefer and more focused cortical arousal effects which subserve "attention" to particular aspects of the organism's environment (Sharpless and Jasper, 1956; Jasper, 1960).

Summary of Arousal Physiology

In the brief foregoing review, the anatomy of what has been termed a *fundamental dimension of behavior* has been touched upon. Needless to say, much detail has been omitted and nothing has been said about specific motivational patterns. In a sense, the material has only dealt with how fast the organism's motor is running, not what direction it is taking. Upon considering the interrelated cortex, hypothalamus, and reticular formation as a unit, together with their multiple relationships with virtually all of the major physical systems in the body, the concept of general arousal seems to have validity. This is particularly apparent when the overlap of the BSRF and the hypothalamus is highlighted. The control of the autonomic nervous system by the hypothalamus, which, in turn, ramifies throughout the body, is just one instance of the generality of effects. Second, of course, is the hypothalamic regulation of the pituitary gland, which integrates a diversity of biochemical systems. Lastly, the fact that all of the organism's sensory systems feed into the reticular formation—and to a considerable extent determine its level of activity—supports the contention that this system represents perhaps an elemental, first-order attempt by the body to organize and integrate motivated behavior.

The findings that areas in the visceral brain, such as the hippocampus and septum, are involved in the arousal process adds an interesting new dimension to this area. It is generally recognized that this limbic area of the brain subserves many functions in such motivational systems as hunger, thirst, sex, and emotional responses. These interrelationships have prompted Grossman (1967, pp. 638) to suggest that the limbic system may, therefore, subserve arousal processes related to internal drive states, whereas the reticular formation, with its multiple inputs from sensory systems, may mediate arousal in response to external stimulation. Granting this as a feasible categorization, the possibilities for studying the interplay between external and internal triggering of the arousal response are interesting. For example, we might ask what effects these systems have on selective attention (presumably for motivationally important external stimuli) and their general effects on behavior.

AROUSAL AND BEHAVIOR

A considerable amount of investigation has gone into attempts to describe the relationship between arousal and the efficiency of various types of performance, ranging all the way from simple reaction-time behaviors to complex concept formation. In this research context some interesting side issues have come to light, particularly concerning the topics of alertness and attention, which bear mention. In the following section, representative studies covering this range of topics will be reviewed.

Reticular Formation and Performance

Perhaps the best-known study in which the reticular formation was directly manipulated with respect to behavioral efficiency is one by Fuster (1958). In this investigation rhesus monkeys were trained to discriminate between two geometric forms which were presented briefly to the subject on each trial. Food was the reward for a correct response. Fuster measured the percentage of correct responses and the time it took for the animal to respond under (*a*) normal conditions and (*b*) under varying intensities of electrical stimulation to the reticular formation. He found that performance improved under moderate reticular stimulation. The intensity of stimulation here seemed to be such as to produce a high degree of behavioral alertness. As a subsidiary finding, he observed that, with reticular stimulation of intensities high enough to produce behavioral signs of alarm (startle reaction, vocalizations, etc.), the task efficiency was reduced.

Comparable findings have been obtained by other investigators (e.g., Lansing et al., 1959; Ogawa, 1963), all of which point to the notion that, in a wakeful organism, there are intensities of reticular activity which are associated with optimal performance. Fuster suggests that this optimal level corresponds to that which produces attentive and alert behavior. This line of reasoning has been extended by other theorists (e.g., Malmo, 1959) who quite logically point out that on either side of this optimal level of reticular activity the organism is either drowsy, bored, overly relaxed, or undergoing some degree of excitement, any of which probably bring about reduced task efficiency.

There is an inherent logic to this view, and pertinent data will be reviewed shortly. Before proceeding, however, the current discussion warrants a small diversion. The terms *alertness* and *attention* have been used frequently in this chapter, but without much specificity. Actually, some very interesting investigations have been carried out attempting to define the neural mechanisms underlying these concepts. Although far from being completely understood, the research to date does provide some important elaborations of the arousal process.

Habituation and Attention

As a preliminary step, let us again review the relationship between sensory input (sight, hearing, etc.), the reticular formation, and the cortex. Figure 2.2 presents a block diagram of these interconnections. Nerve impulses in the auditory system, for example, have essentially two routes to the primary auditory area of the cortex. The first is the rather direct line from the sense organ, through sensory nuclei in the thalamus, to the sensory cortex. The other is the more indirect route through the reticular formation, producing a general discharge in this system which, in turn, sends projections in a diffuse way to all parts of the cortex. The same relationship seems to hold for other sensory systems as well. It is possible to record electrical activity at various points in this over-all system, some of the important ones (to be discussed below) are indicated by the letters *A*, *B*, and *C* on the diagram. Now back to the story.

The fact that we rather quickly become inattentive to a stimulus which is presented over and over again is a familiar experience. This *habituation* phenomenon appears to be a function of changes that take place in reticular formation activity (Jasper, 1958). If, for example, a tone is sounded, a sleeping animal will usually be awakened by this stimulus. This process will also be reflected in a rapid change in the animal's EEG record from one of sleep to activation. If, however, this set of circumstances reoccurs, say 15 to 20 times, the animal will continue to sleep when the tone is sounded; of course, there will also be no change from the EEG sleep pattern. Of importance, however, is the observation that, under these circumstances, the auditory signal to the sensory cortex (measured at *A*) is not reduced (Sharpless and Jasper, 1956). Thus the habituation phenomenon does not seem to be caused by any changes in the specific sen-

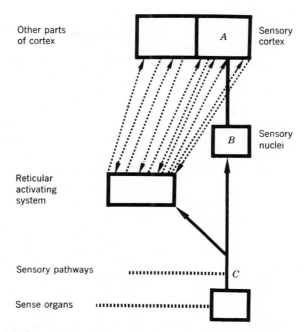

Figure 2.2 Block diagram of interconnections between the sense organs, reticular formation, thalamic relay nuclei and the cortex. [Adapted from D. Bindra, *Motivation: A Systematic Reinterpretation.* New York: Ronald Press, 1959, p. 255. *(Courtesy of D. Bindra.)*]

sory-cortical channel but by alterations in the diffuse reticular-cortical system. This same general pattern has also been obtained with awake animals, in which a frequently occurring stimulus loses its attention-getting value.

The concept of habituation implies that the reduced response to stimulation is the result of some active, centrally mediated inhibitory process rather than mere fatigue in a sensory system. The weight of evidence suggests that habituation can be observed at all levels of the sensory pathways, from the first synapse (neural junction) beyond the receptor up to the sensory cortex (Hernandez-Peon, 1961).

There is considerable evidence that portions of the reticular formation exert an influence on sensory processes. For example, electrical stimulation of the midbrain reticular formation has been demonstrated to either inhibit or enhance potentials in sensory systems. These include somatosensory pathways (Hagbarth and Kerr, 1954), the visual system (Granit, 1955), auditory pathways (Galambos, 1956), and olfactory fibers (Hernandez-Peon et al., 1960). Other related areas of the brain also appear to be involved in these sensory effects. For example, impulses in the auditory system can be enhanced or inhibited by stimulation of sites near the superior olive (Rasmussen, 1953) (see Appendix); in the somatosensory system, mediated by sites in the parietal cortex and cerebellum (Hagbarth and Kerr, 1954); and of sympathetic fibers of the autonomic nervous system (Loewenstein, 1956). Lastly, the cerebral cortex influences incoming sensory signals through an efferent corticofugal system (downward projecting) which apparently operates both directly and through lower brain centers (Adey et al., 1957) on sensory systems. In effect, the cortex to a degree, can influence and modify its own input through this efferent system.

The reverse of this habituation process has also been demonstrated, indicating the probable role of the BSRF in attention. Recording from a single neuron in the lateral geniculate nucleus of the cat (a thalamic relay station in the visual system; *B* in Figure 2.2), Ogawa (1963) found that the rate of electric discharge in this nucleus to a flash of light was enhanced by reticular stimulation. This effect could not be accounted for by the spread of electrical activity from the BSRF to the lateral geniculate nucleus since the effect far outlasted the reticular stimulation. In another phase of this study, Ogawa demonstrated that stimulation of the BSRF increased the "resolving power" of the nucleus in that it was now able to respond more discretely to a rapid train of light flashes. Hence the increased activity in the reticular formation seemed to have a direct effect on the capability of the sensory system to transmit visual information.

That this phenomenon is related to attention is brought out by an earlier study by Jouvet (1957). Using human subjects and measuring EEG discharge in the visual cortex (point *A* in Figure 2.2), it was found that a greater cortical response occurred to flashes of light when subjects were instructed to "pay attention" to the visual stimuli.

We have here, then, a further delineation of reticular effects. Whereas earlier their role in general arousal was discussed, the present evidence suggests that there may be some focused reticular-cortical processes involved in the habituation or enhancement of information being transmitted on specific sensory channels. Current thinking on this matter suggests that the upper part of the reticular formation, at the level of the thalamus, may be involved in these more transient and localized effects. Regardless of its locus, however, this preliminary evidence represents the beginning of a research effort to clarify the neurology of such traditionally difficult questions as: How does the organism select some stimuli for its attention, and ignore others? This age-old question concerning the nature of awareness and the direction of consciousness is finally succumbing to empirical investigation.

If we consider the problem of attention from a common-sense point of view, there are several factors which might be considered. Certainly novel or unusual stimuli claim our attention, as do stimuli which, through prior learning, have proved to be important (see Berlyne, 1960, for a thorough review of this subject). However, the problem remains of conceptualizing how, when we are focused on one aspect of the environment, we seem to be able to screen out other equally intense, though irrelevant, stimuli. A hint about the neurological processes involved in this selective perception is provided in a very fascinating study by Hernandez-Peon et al. (1956).

In this study, recording electrodes were placed in the cochlear nucleus of a cat. This placement is considerably different from those in the earlier studies in that it is one of the first relay stations beyond the sense organ itself, in this case, the ear. Thus it corresponds to point C in Figure 2.2. When a series of clicking sounds were presented, a well-defined and strong electric discharge occurred in the cochlear nucleus. The cat appeared to be alert and attending to this auditory stimulus. If, however, a new stimulus was introduced which claimed the cat's attention, a mouse (in an enclosed bottle), for example, being placed in his cage or the application of painful stimuli, the cochlear discharge was markedly reduced. This diminution of electrical response took place, of course, even though the auditory clicks were presented at the same intensity as before.

This again is an example of the fact that sensory systems are not only afferent, i.e., transmit information from the peripheral sense organs to the brain. Here is an instance where some central process, related to attention, also has an efferent effect on the peripheral sensory systems, in this case bringing about an inhibition in electrical activity at a site relatively close to the sense organ itself. This took place when the organism's focus of attention was directed to another sensory channel. It is likely that the reticular formation plays a role in this process, although it was not specifically studied in the foregoing investigation.

This effect has been observed in other sensory systems as well, such as the visual (Hernandez-Peon et al., 1957) and the olfactory and skin senses (Palestini et al., 1959). The fact that this "attentional" phenomenon can be mediated at levels below the cortex has been demonstrated by Hernandez-Peon (1961) using decorticated cats and by Galambos and Sheatz using cats and monkeys. Again it appears that this selective attention may be mediated by portions of the reticular formation, although there is evidence that orientation to important external stimuli is influenced by limbic structures such as the hippocampus (Grastyan et al., 1959) and the cortex itself.

Very clearly a great amount of further work is needed to clarify the neurology of attention. The door, however, has been opened and the glimpse provided suggests that the reticular formation is an indispensable part of this process. We can now return to the more general topic of the correlation between arousal and performance, with some insight into the neurological and sensory events which underlie the relationship.

Induced Arousal and Human Task Efficiency

In the material reviewed up until now, based on animal research, the following points stand out: (*a*) the level of BSRF activity is related to the amount of sensory input, cortical stimulation of the BSRF, and excitation by circulating epinephrine; (*b*) reticular activity (including the hypothalamic connections), in turn, influences cortical, sensory, sympathetic, skeletomuscular, and diverse biochemical systems; (*c*) behaviorally these influences are reflected in the organism's degree of wakefulness and its perceptual and neuromuscular efficiency. Considering these widespread effects it is not surprising that several theorists have attempted to relate arousal level with behavioral efficiency on more complex intellectual tasks in humans. Here, of course, it would be impossible to perform the surgery required for precise neurological recordings or stimulation, so investigators have had to rely on the more accessible, peripheral measures, notably autonomic recordings. These, it will be recalled, are physiologically part of the over-all arousal system.

Perhaps the most universal hypothesis relating arousal to human performance is the *inverted-U relationship* (Freeman, 1940). According to this notion, as the subject's arousal level proceeds from, for example, drowsiness to alertness, there is a progressive increase in the efficiency of performance. Similarly, as arousal goes even higher, say from alertness to high excitement, there is a progressive decrease in task efficiency. Thus it is suggested that there is a middle range of arousal which is associated with optimal performance.

Any number of studies have provided support for the inverted-U hypothesis. Several representative investigators will be mentioned here. Freeman (1940), using spontaneous changes in skin conductance as a measure of arousal, found that subjects showed the fastest responding in a reaction-time experiment at intermediate conductance levels. In the same vein, Stennett (1957) experimentally produced differing levels of muscle potentials and skin conductance by using various incentives and found that maximum performance on a tracking task occurred at intermediate levels of the physiological measures. In yet another variation, Wood and Hokanson (1965) produced differing levels of arm muscle tension by having subjects pull on weights. The amount of weight to be pulled was some fraction of the maximum weight they could sustain. The task used was a simple symbol-matching performance. Figure 2.3 shows (*a*) the change in a physiological measure (heart rate) and (*b*) the change in per-

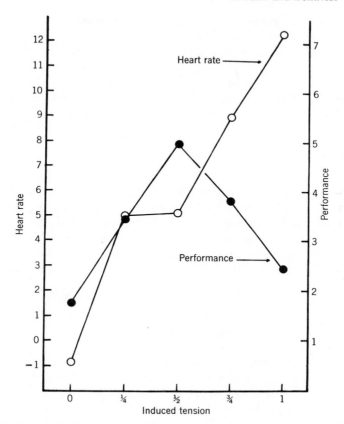

Figure 2.3 Relationship between heart rate increase, task performance change, and induced muscular tension. [From Wood and Hokanson (original research, 1964.)]

formance rate, both as a function of induced muscle tension. As can be seen, the heart-rate graph shows progressively greater elevations as the induced muscle tension is increased, whereas the performance curve is in the shape of an inverted U.

Although many other studies demonstrate much the same data utilizing other perceptual-motor tasks and a wider range of autonomic measures, the arousal-performance relationship does not appear to be this pure and simple. For example, an inverted-U function was not found in several studies utilizing more intricate tasks, e.g., complex symbol-matching (Hokanson and Burgess, 1964), serial verbal learning (Wood, 1964), and concept formation (White, 1965). Thus the task-complexity variable appears to be a limiting factor in studies done to date and awaits more precise experimentation. An additional problem is found in the use of autonomic measures as indicators of "arousal." Lacey (1956) has pointed out the remarkable individual differences in the patterning of autonomic responses that occur between subjects, thus making it a very risky procedure to utilize a single peripheral measure as representative of the organism's arousal status. Here again, considerably more work is required to detail the more subtle relationships between autonomic patterns and behavior.

DREAMS

A discussion of the sleep-excitement dimension would be incomplete without a description of some of the research work done on dreams. This topic, in the past often relegated to the province of psychoanalysis, has recently undergone intensive study from a physiological point of view, with some very provocative results. The findings seem to have implications for both general theories of central nervous system organization and the nature of certain abnormal processes.

The beginnings of modern dream research started in the laboratory of Dr. Nathaniel Kleitman at the University of Chicago in the early 1950s. Human subjects who were participating in sleep research were observed to have periodic episodes of very quick and rapid eye movements beneath their closed lids while apparently asleep. These rapid eye movements (REM) were typically accompanied by marked fluctuations in respiration and heart rate, and the EEG changed from the usual large, slow, and regular waves of deep sleep to a low-voltage, desynchronized pattern (Aserinsky and Kleitman, 1953; Kleitman, 1963). Furthermore, when subjects were awakened from this rather unusual state of sleep, they almost inevitably reported a dream, but when awakened from other than REM sleep, they rarely reported dreams (e.g., Dement and Kleitman, 1957). This pattern of rapid eye movements, autonomic variability, EEG desynchronization, and dream state suggested that a unique and, perhaps, paradoxical condition of sleep was being studied—a contention which subsequent research has borne out.

Individual Patterns of REM Sleep

Prior to the recent data on dreams, most people assumed that dreams were relatively rare events, perhaps largely because of difficulties in recalling one's ideation after a night's sleep. It now seems clear, after a decade of intensive dream research, that the average young adult spends about 20 to 25% of his sleep time in this REM state. Although individuals vary in the patterning of REM periods, on the average it appears as if a brief dream state occurs after about 90 minutes of sleep; thereafter longer episodes occur at approximately intervals of 1 to 1½ hours. Also there seems to be a tendency for greater incidence of REM sleep in the last third of a night's sleep (Dement, 1965). Individuals tend to be rather stable in their sequencing of sleep states, so that it appears that each of us has a characteristic pattern. Indeed, with a subject who has been studied extensively, it appears possible to predict when and for how long he will dream during a night's sleep (Dement, 1965).

Deprivation of REM Sleep

One aspect of dream research which has provoked great interest consists of those studies in which subjects are prevented from engaging in REM sleep. In one such study (Dement, 1960) carefully selected human volunteers were permitted their usual sleep in the laboratory, with the exception of being awakened at the first signs of each REM phase. (Rapid eye movements, desynchronized EEG patterns, or loss of muscle tonus in the chin can serve as criteria for the onset of dreaming.) This procedure was continued for five successive nights, thus not depriving these subjects of sleep as such, but preventing them from engaging in the REM type of sleep. Control subjects were awakened for comparable lengths of time, but during non-REM phases of sleep. Two results emerged from this study:

1. Subjects deprived of REM sleep frequently complained of psychological discomfort, anxiety, and a tendency to overeat. These complaints did not occur with the control subjects.

2. After the experiment, when subjects were permitted uninterrupted sleep, the REM-deprived subjects dreamed approximately 60% more than they had on the preexperimental baseline nights.

In subsequent studies, the finding of psychological discomfort as a result of REM deprivation has been inconsistent, no doubt reflecting individual differences in responsiveness to this kind of deficit. However, in virtually every published study involving interrupted REM sleep, both with humans and animals, there have been observed compensatory increases in REM states when the subject is allowed to sleep through the night (Jouvet, 1965).

In one particularly exacting study (Dement, 1965) three healthy human volunteers were deprived of REM sleep for 16 days. Midway through the vigil one of the subjects entered directly into the REM phase upon falling asleep, a pattern not characteristic of this person. The tendency to begin immediately dreaming was so pronounced that the experimenter had to awaken the subject almost continually to prevent REM sleep.

Toward the end of the 16-day period, another subject appeared to start dreaming the moment his eyes closed, a markedly abnormal pattern typically seen only in certain cases of psychosis, drug withdrawal, or narcolepsy (a clinical syndrome involving a tendency to fall asleep at inappropriate times). On the first night after the experiment was over, this subject dreamed 120% more than was normal for him, after which he returned to his usual pattern.

Taken together, the reliable tendency to make up for lost dream time and the frequent reports of psychological distress when dream deprived suggest a need to dream (or for REM sleep). This seemed to be one of the most provocative outcomes of REM research. It places dream research in the realm of motivation and also draws attention to the possibility of gaining insights into certain abnormal processes which may be related to sleep or REM deprivation.

Naturally, experimenters have been cautious in carrying REM deprivation studies with humans to extreme lengths for fear of causing some permanent damage. Several studies, however, have utilized animal subjects (primarily cats) and introduced prolonged periods of REM loss (Jouvet, 1965; Dement, 1965). Deprivation as long as 70 days produced marked increases in eating, hypersexuality, and abnormal degrees of restlessness. The intensity of these behaviors was such that, if observed in humans, it would undoubtedly have led to psychiatric hospitalization.

In addition, with these long REM deprivations, it appears that the organism reaches a limit in being able to make up for lost REM time. Both Jouvet and Dement, in their studies of prolonged deprivation, found that the greater REM loss, the more compensatory REM time when the animal was allowed uninterrupted sleep, but only up to a point. Jouvet found, for example, that after a total of 24 hours of deprivation, there was a 45% increase in subsequent REM sleep in cats. With 72 hours deprivation, there was a 60% rise, and this seemed to be the limit of compensation for a single night. With cats deprived for many days longer, the 60% value was not surpassed. Of course, much of the compensation may take place in later nights of normal sleep, this catching-up process going on for as long as 10 days.

Biochemical Processes and REM Sleep

Taking the data on REM deprivation as a whole, it appears that there is a need for REM sleep; moreover, that this is likely a physiological as well as psychological process. Perhaps the psychological distress reported by many human subjects after dream deprivation is a response of the organism to a developing physical penalty.

Dement (1965) has suggested the possibility that the dream state is produced basically by biochemical processes in the brain, which are in some way dissipated or transformed during the REM state. With prolonged REM deprivation, as in the cat studies mentioned previously, there might be an accumulation of the chemical to the extent that spillage into the spinal fluid, for example, could occur. With this general hypothesis in mind, Henry et al. (1965) withdrew spinal fluid from very REM deprived cats and injected it into cats who had normal sleep histories. Although there were some complications due to the complex transfer procedures involved, the receiver cats showed a definite increase in REM sleep after the injections. Here then is suggestive evidence of a biochemical influence in the development of this paradoxical sleep.

Matsumoto and Jouvet (1964) provide some indirect evidence relative to the possible biochemical trigger involved. Dopa, a drug chemically related to noradrenalin, was found to restore temporarily suppressed REM activity. This suggests the possibility that some aspect of this family of energizing chemicals plays a role in the development of the dream state. Furthermore, certain nuclei in the pons, which have been implicated in REM sleep, have been shown to respond to noradrenalin (Jouvet, 1965).

Weitzman et al. (1965) traced the rise and fall of adrenal cortex hormones throughout nights of sleep, and found that levels of these "stress" hormones show a correlation with periods of REM sleep. Similarly, Armstrong et al. (1965) found that patients with duodenal ulcers had significantly higher gastric secretions during REM periods of sleep, whereas normal control subjects showed no particular variations in gastric output.

Thus there is an accumulation of evidence that REM sleep is concomitant with periods of arousal; biochemicals ordinarily associated with excitation are at elevated levels; and subjects report vivid mentation. Furthermore, with dream deprivation, there is an increase in feelings of psychological distress, a heightening of needs and appetites (e.g., voracious overeating and hypersexuality), and, with extreme deprivation, behavior patterns which have been judged to be abnormal.

Implications

It has been suggested by Dement (1965) and others that REM sleep in adults may be remnants of biologically important processes in the developing young. In infancy, for example, it is possible that the brain activity associated with REM sleep plays an important role in survival by triggering or mobilizing drive-oriented behaviors. This contention gains some support from the observations of sucking movements made by infants during REM phases, penile erections in humans, and the generally increased drives of REM-deprived animals. In adults, dreams may play a similar, though reduced, mobilizing role with respect to biological drives while in addition, reflecting complex societal influences and constraints on these drives.

With respect to abnormal processes, there is reasonable evidence to suggest that, with prolonged REM deprivation, clinically significant symptoms may occur. The voracious drives, general restlessness, and the rapid onset of dreamlike thought are reminiscent of certain psychoticlike reactions. The possibility that some biochemical accumulation occurring with REM deprivation contributes to this process raises an important issue for researchers in the mental health area. What the neuronal-biochemical-behavioral processes are in the potentially psychotic patient which bring about the abnormal developments to begin with are, of course, the longer-range areas of clinical investigation.

Summary

There seems to be an adequate supply of evidence to suggest that a fundamental integration of biochemical, sensory, autonomic, neuromuscular, and central nervous system (cortical) events takes place at the level of reticular formation and hypothalamus. Aside from the possibility that this system may be involved in some selective aspects of attention, the reticular mechanisms seem to affect primarily the intensive dimension of behavior, not its direction.

In addition, there is little doubt that the BSRF and posterior hypothalamus are critical areas concerned with sleep and degrees of wakefulness. This area of research, therefore, represents a possible neurological approach to the traditionally difficult problem of defining consciousness. Related to this are its demonstrated effects on sensory phenomena, both in enhancing the cortical signals of "relevant" stimuli and inhibiting sensory impulses of irrelevant input.

Of particular interest (and controversy) are the still early stages of research on the specific neural events subserving the phenomena of habituation, selective attention, and the interplay between internal drive states and external stimuli in determining the organism's orientation to the environment. As a potential outgrowth of these topics, perhaps future researchers will be able to delineate more specifically the neurological processes which underlie the inverted-U relationship obtained between arousal and performance in humans.

As the reader may have discerned, the physical systems reviewed in this chapter also play a major role in emotional behavior. For the sake of clarity, however, this area will be touched on in a later chapter dealing with pain. In the intervening chapters, the physiology of such basic motivational systems as hunger, thirst, temperature, and sex will be covered.

III

Behavior Related to Food and Eating

The factors controlling the intake of food are multiple and, as yet, not completely understood. However, the attempts carried out over the past 60 years to describe this complex network of controls tell a fascinating story of scientific endeavor—the piecing together of the various elements of a difficult puzzle to the point where we can now begin to make out the picture. The plan of this chapter, therefore, is to describe separately the different areas of research bearing on the puzzle and then to present an integrated summary of the material at the close of the chapter.

As a starting point, let us consider some of the well-documented facts concerning the actual behavior of eating. Any theory concerning the physiological controls on eating must, of course, be in keeping with these behavioral data.

Looking just at the amount of food ingested, the following generalization can be made: (*a*) given an unlimited supply, the experimental organism (usually a laboratory rat) will ingest enough food to keep its *weight* constant (Teitelbaum, 1961); (*b*) if the available food is diluted or its caloric properties reduced, the organism will increase the amount ingested to maintain its intake of *calories* at a constant level (Adolph, 1947; Richter, 1953); (*c*) if the organism's energy requirements are increased, for example, by making him engage in violent activity or reducing the environmental temperature, he will compensate by increasing his intake. Moreover, under these circumstances, if given a choice between a high-energy food such as dextrose and equally sweet tasting, but nonnutritive saccharine, the organism will markedly increase his intake of dextrose (Griffiths and Gallagher, 1953; Brobeck, 1960).

These processes are complicated further by numerous observations that organisms will also alter their food-intake patterns in response to particular bodily deficits or excesses. For example, during pregnancy the normal levels of sodium and phosphorous, among other substances, are reduced in the body. Given a free choice, the organism adjusts its intake to make up these deficiencies. Furthermore, intake patterns return to normal after weaning (Richter, 1942). The same shifts in ingestion to meet *known* deficits in the body have been demonstrated for salt (Richter and Eckert, 1938), calcium (Richter, 1939), and most of the B complex vitamins (Scott and Quint, 1946), among others. On the other hand, the production of specific excesses in the body, via direct introduction into the stomach, leads to compensatory drops in the intake of these substances (Stellar, Hymen and Samet, 1954; Richter, 1939).

All these results raise a variety of questions pertaining to the nature of the controlling mechanisms involved. How does the body know when its general food stores are being depleted or when a specific substance is below its normal level? By what means is this state of affairs communicated to the central nervous system? What are the mechanisms in the central nervous system that start the organism eating or looking for food, and then bring about a cessation of eating when the body's supplies are replenished? In short, what is the relationship between the internal state of affairs of the body and the organism's food-related behavior? The very fascinating experimental work that has been carried out in attempting to answer these questions is really the subject matter of this chapter.

VARIABLES ASSOCIATED WITH TASTE

The role of the sensations of taste in regulating food intake are as yet incompletely understood; but the evidence accumulated thus far assigns an important, though not indispensable, role to this system. To begin with, let us locate this system and note some of its characteristics.

The nerves concerned with taste leave the tongue as the VII, IX, and X cranial nerves and make their first synaptic junction in the brain in certain areas of the medulla. These connections were first described in the early anatomical studies of Allen (1923). More recently, Halpern (1959) was able to record evoked electrical activity in these medullary areas when taste solutions were applied to the tongue. The next station is in a rather small area of the thalamus (medial tip of the ventral nucleus), and again, electrical activity can be measured from this area when taste solutions are placed on the tongue (Benjamin and Akert, 1959). From here fibers project to the cerebral cortex eventuating in an area that is adjacent to both the general sensory mouth area and the motor area concerned with chewing (foot of the postcentral gyrus).

Of particular interest in this system is the fact that evoked electrical activity at the peripheral taste nerves, medullary, and thalamic levels all have the same characteristics (Pfaffman, 1961). The higher the concentration of substance in solution placed on the tongue, the greater the electric discharge in the nerve. The concentration–electric-discharge curves are the same whether recorded from the peripheral nerve, medulla, or thalamus. Apparently this system relays sensory information all the way to the thalamus with little change in its intensive dimension. As yet, there has been no report of successfully recorded cortical responses to taste stimuli; however, Pfaffman (1961) suggests that perhaps the electrical activity in the cortex is more complex and, therefore, more difficult to record.

To complete this description of the classical taste pathways, the effects of specific destruction of certain of these areas should be mentioned. When the taste area in the thalamus is destroyed, there is a sharp reduction in the behavioral response to both normally aversive and preferred solutions, i.e., discriminations on the basis of taste are severely impaired (Benjamin and Akert, 1959). When, however, the cortical taste area is ablated, there are no measurable effects on behavior toward preferred solutions and only a transient effect on aversions, i.e., a minimal change when compared to thalamic damage. These results have led Pfaffman (1961) to speculate that there must be other neural structures to which collaterals are sent, probably in the limbic system or hypothalamus, also concerned with taste. As we shall see later in this chapter, there is some evidence in support of this contention.

Now back to the main question: Does this taste system play a role in regulating intake, or is intake controlled solely by postingestion factors? Consider the following experiments which attempt to resolve this issue. Berkun et al. (1952) surgically prepared their experimental rats with permanently implanted fistulas (a tube inserted into the stomach through which substances can be passed, thereby by-passing the mouth). In one group of rats, milk was injected directly into the stomach, whereas a second group drank the same amount of milk normally. Following these prefeeding treatments, the rats were given free access to milk and the additional amount drunk was recorded. It was found that normal prefeeding led to a greater subsequent reduction in milk intake. This points to an oral (taste?) factor in the cessation of eating.

In a study along similar lines Weiner and Stellar (1951) first measured the preferences and aversions of rats for various salt solutions. They then introduced a fistula into the esophagus of each rat. Thus, when a rat drank a solution, it received the normal taste sensations in the mouth, but the liquid was drained out through the fistula before reaching the stomach. Under these conditions they found that the rats preferences and aversions were unaltered from what they were in their normal feeding state. Thus again, the evidence suggests that a taste factor operates independently of postingestion factors in the regulation of intake.

In spite of the evidence pointing to oral factors, there is also ample evidence that regulation occurs in their absence. This was already hinted at in the Berkun study where prefeeding directly into the stomach did have an effect on subsequent ingestion. Perhaps the neatest demonstration of the postingestion control comes in a study by Epstein and Teitelbaum (1962). These investigators prepared their rats with a permanent tube going into the stomach; in addition, they had the tube connected to a pipetting machine which could automatically provide a squirt of liquid food directly into the stomach. This apparatus was, in turn, made part of a Skinner box, so that the rat pressing the bar in the box provided a squirt of food into the stomach. Naturally then, oral sensations had no way of coming into play in this experiment and the rat received all of its food intragastrically. After some preliminary learning, it was found that the rats controlled their intake just as precisely as normal rats; i.e., as mentioned in the introduction to this chapter, they made all the necessary behavioral adjustments to maintain constant weight and caloric intake when the size and composition of the squirts were varied.

Taking an overview of these studies concerned with the relative importance of taste versus postingestion factors in regulating intake, several tentative conclusions can be drawn: (*a*) there is strong evidence that the overall intake of nutriments can be regulated in the absence of oral factors; (*b*) there is also some evidence that oral factors alone can control the intake of substances which the animal can discriminate via taste; (*c*) in normal feeding situations, both sets of factors are operating, but the precise nature of how they work together has not yet been worked out.

One final question has to be raised concerning taste. It was mentioned earlier that organisms appear to be capable of compensating for specific internal deficits by ingesting more of these substances. How do these compensatory alterations in intake come about? Carl Pfaffman, one of the leading investigators in the area, has attempted to investigate these physiological-behavioral relationships, but as yet, the question is still unanswered. Pfaffman hypothesized that the *taste thresholds* for the deficient substances were lowered; i.e., the organism became selectively more sensitive and hence could discriminate these substances more readily. This notion was tested electrophysiologically by Pfaffman and Bare in 1950. They measured the electric discharge in the taste nerves coming from the tongue in response to varying concentrations of salt solutions. These neural responses were obtained from both normal rats and those who had their adrenal glands removed (thereby making them salt deficient). Although they obtained the usual finding that the neural discharge is increased as the salt concentration was increased, there was no difference between the normal and the adrenalectomized rats. These negative results with respect to his hypothesis were also obtained in a behavioral threshold study by Carr (1952).

As yet then, there has been no really satisfactory explanation of the mechanisms involved in how the organism makes up for these specific deficits. The physiological-behavioral linkage evidently occurs further back in the nervous system and not at the peripheral receptor level. Pfaffman's suggestion, mentioned earlier, that the classical taste pathways may also be connected to the limbic-hypothalamic system provides food for thought, but these considerations must wait until this area of the brain has been covered in the next portion of the chapter.

VARIABLES ASSOCIATED WITH THE CENTRAL NERVOUS SYSTEM

Although some structures of the central nervous system have already been mentioned in connection with taste, perhaps the most important with respect to eating has yet to be mentioned—the hypothalamus. As has been indicated in earlier chapters, it is one of the major coordinating centers in the nervous system, having intimate connections not only with the cortex but also with the autonomic nervous system, the endocrine system (via its close association with the pituitary gland), and other neural structures associated with arousal. In addition, it is a richly vascularized area of the brain, so that it is in an anatomically strategic location to provide a chemical-neural integration in the body. With respect to eating, there are two important parts of the hypothalamus to which most attention has been devoted: the ventromedial area and the lateral hypothalamus (see Figure A.3).

Ventromedial Area

It has been medically known for some time that a tumor in the region of the hypothalamus leads to tremendous gains in weight (obesity). A controversy raged during the early part of this century as to whether the critical structure involved was the hypothalamus itself or the adjacent pituitary gland. The resolution of this dispute had to await the development of an instrument during the 1930's which was precise enough to produce small, discrete lesions in specific areas of this region. Using this stereotaxic instrument, Hetherington and Ranson (1940, 1942) did the critical experiments demonstrating that hypothalamic lesions alone were responsible for the obesity. The particular area of the hypothalamus that was implicated was the ventromedial nucleus.

Since these early studies a great deal of work has been carried out delineating the action of this small nucleus. Teitelbaum and his coworkers have done the most extensive research on the obesity which develops following these lesions. Following destruction of the ventromedial area the development of the clinical syndrome (called *hypothalamic hyperphagia*) takes place in two phases: the dynamic and the static phases. During the former stage the animal greatly increases its intake of food. It eats no more often than normals, if fed on a liquid diet, but it does eat longer at each meal, increasing its intake by two or three times (Teitelbaum and Campbell, 1958). After approximately 30 to 60 days of constant weight gain, the animal's weight levels off and its food intake drops back to only slightly above normal. This now is the static phase of the syndrome (Teitelbaum, 1961). Figures 3.1 and 3.2 show the development of hyperphagia in the rat.

What are the mechanisms involved in this weight gain? Perhaps it is really a result of a metabolic disturbance brought about by the lesions in

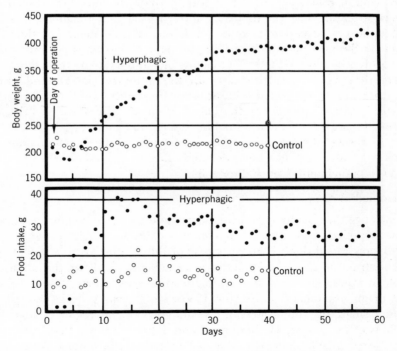

Figure 3.1 Food intake and body weight of a hyperphagic (lesion in ventromedial nucleus) and normal rat. (Adapted from P. Teitelbaum, in *Nebraska Symposium on Motivation*, Lincoln: University of Nebraska Press, 1961, p. 41.)

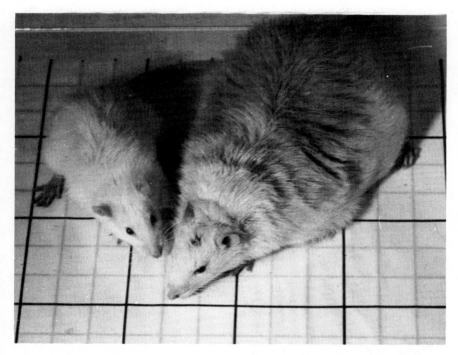

Figure 3.2 Comparison of normal and hyperphagic rat. Prior to lesion of ventro-medial nucleus both rats weighed the same. In their present conditions the normal rat weighs 320 grams vs. 1,020 grams for the hyperphagic rat. (*Courtesy of Dr. Douglas Grimsley.*)

the ventromedial nucleus. This hypothesis was ruled out in an extensive series of studies by Brobeck (e.g., Brobeck et al., 1943) and Brooks (e.g., Brooks et al., 1946). The metabolic processes of hyperphagics are not different from those of normals.

A second possibility is that in some way the sense of taste has been altered, so that the organism is not sensitive to the tastes of various foods and, hence, indiscriminately takes in all food substances offered. Actually, the opposite is the case, at least with operates in the static phase. Hyperphagic rats have been found to be exceptionally finicky about their food. If a nonnutritive additive is included in the diet of normals, they will increase their intake to maintain constant caloric levels. Hyperphagics decrease their intake. Similarly, normals will tolerate quite a lot of bitter-tasting additives in their food, whereas hyperphagics will not. Conversely, if the food is sweetened, normals will adjust their intake to maintain again constant calories, whereas the hyperphagic eats more. So, if anything, the operated animal appears to be more, rather than less, sensitive to taste factors. (Teitelbaum, 1961).

Finally, there is the possibility that the animals "motivational" state is increased as a result of the hypothalamic damage. This more general hypothesis can also be ruled out by the observations that hyperphagics will not work as hard, nor tolerate as much electric shock as normals, in order to get food (Miller et al., 1950; Teitelbaum, 1957).

We are left, then, with the observation that the organism with ventromedial lesions simply does not stop eating as normals do—suggesting that this particular area in the hypothalamus is a critical structure concerned with satiation. If it is true that this is a so-called stop center, then in normals an increase in activity in this center should be accompanied by a cessation of eating, and conversely, when the nucleus is destroyed, the organism should have difficulty in stopping its eating. This is, indeed, the case. In normal rats, if the ventromedial nucleus is electrically stimulated via an implanted electrode or chemically stimulated by means of a nerve stimulant introduced through an implanted tube (cannula), ongoing eating is stopped. As a matter of fact, the organism will spit out food in its mouth upon receiving stimulation (Wyrwicka and Drobrzecka, 1960; Epstein, 1960).

Now then, part of the picture is beginning to take shape. A structure has been located in a strategic area of the central nervous system that appears to be directly implicated in the stopping of eating. Destroy it, and the animal does not stop as readily. Stimulate it, and the organism stops immediately. As an aside, it should be mentioned that there are other parts of the brain which produce somewhat the same effects, but not in as striking and permanent way. These other areas include parts of the thalamus, temporal lobes, frontal lobes, and midbrain. The current view is that the hypothalamus lies at the center of a larger "feeding system," with the ventromedial nucleus being the key in the satiation mechanism (see Erlich, 1964). Now the problem becomes one of identifying the normal processes taking place in the body that increase activity in the ventromedial nucleus and thereby bring about a cessation of eating. As will be seen, there are any number of such processes and probably more to be discovered.

Internal Controls on Ventromedial Nucleus

One of the most persistent notions concerning the elicitation of electrical activity in this satiation center is that the cells in the nucleus are sensitive to changes in the composition of the blood. This view maintains that, as the organism ingests food, which in turn is transformed into substances circulating through the vascular system, chemically sensitive cells in the nucleus are thereby triggered, thus producing a cessation of eating.

Foremost among these biochemical hypotheses is Mayer's *glucostatic* theory (1952), which suggests that the ventromedial nucleus is sensitive to the changes in the dynamics of blood sugar. Although apparently no simple relationship is to be found here, the critical events seem to be related to glucose uptake (the difference between arterial blood sugar before entering an organ and venous content after leaving the organ). Anand et al. (1961) reported finding altered electrical activity in the ventromedial area produced by elevated blood sugar levels, thus supporting Mayer's theory. In a later study Anand et al. (1964) demonstrated that the activity in single neurons in the ventromedial nucleus changed in response to alterations in the difference between arterial and venous glucose. That this area appears to be selectively sensitive to glucose was shown by Mayer and Marshall (1956) who found that a gold-glucose compound was deposited in the ventromedial hypothalamus.

A related hypothesis suggests that the cells in this "satiation" center are sensitive to some biochemical substance related to the status of the animal's fat deposits (lipostatic theory). In the operated animal, of course, this circulating substance has no center to work on, and thus the organism does not stop eating. Relating ventromedial activity to weight and fat deposits is certainly consistent with Teitelbaum's observations that, once the hyperphagic's weight has stabilized, it regulates its intake much as normals do. Although it is true that hyperphagic rats metabolize fats at about normal rates while on a restricted feeding routine, when they are given unrestricted access to food, this metabolic rate is greatly reduced (Bates et al., 1955). This suggests that a specific disorder relating to fat metabolism may also be involved in the development of hyperphagia. It is likely that this unusual synthesis of fat is an outgrowth of the drastic overeating that takes place. In the rat the change in synthesis rate does not appear until a time after the lesions have been made, although the increased food intake begins immediately after recovery from surgery (Tepperman et al., 1943). Mayer (1955) has suggested that the glucostatic mechanisms may regulate short-term fluctuations in eating, but that the dynamics of fat metabolism may control longer-range food intake. Furthermore, Teitelbaum (1961) reports that, if normal rats are made obese before they are operated on, their weight gain following ventromedial lesions is small, bringing them up to a weight that hyperphagics normally attain. Thus there is reasonable, although not critical, evidence that fat deposits and associated biochemical products in the blood may also innervate the stop center (Kennedy, 1952).

Another class of receptors also seems to be involved—those related to distention of the stomach. Paintal (1953) discovered stretch receptors in the stomach that respond to gastric distention and noted that their upward projections are via the vagus nerve (the main sensory pathway to the brain from this region). Furthermore, Sharma et al. (1961) noted that gastric distention produces increased electrical activity in the ventromedial nucleus. Thus, besides the biochemical controls on the ventromedial nucleus mentioned earlier, there is good evidence of direct mechanical-neural control emanating from the stomach.

Finally, control over the satiation center has been related to thermal factors (thermostatic theory). Brobeck (1957) has pointed out that the ingestion of food is accompanied by increased heat production and has suggested that there may be thermal receptors in the hypothalamus that respond to these temperature changes. In support of this theory is the finding of Andersson and Larsson (1961) that local cooling of the hypothalamus brings about eating, whereas warming is related to a cessation of eating.

Thus we can see a multiplicity of pathways by which hypothalamic activity is controlled. None of these routes to the ventromedial nucleus appears to be indispensable in bringing about increased activity in the nucleus and the consequent inhibition of eating, but certainly the central role of the nucleus itself is highlighted. There is little wonder then that, when the nucleus is destroyed, the very heart of the inhibitory mechanism is lost and the animal cannot stop eating.

Lateral Hypothalamus

Destruction of the lateral hypothalamus results in a condition known as *aphagia*, the inability of the organism to eat or drink, resulting in eventual death. The syndrome was first described in some detail by Anand and Brobeck in 1951 and more recently by Teitelbaum (1961). In the latter work, the course of the syndrome was spelled out more precisely. After the operation, the animal does not eat or drink and, as a matter of fact, will not swallow food placed in its mouth and even shakes off loose food stuck to its paws. If the animal is kept alive, after several days it will begin to eat very palatable foods (e.g., cookies) but still does not drink. During the third stage, if water balance is artificially maintained, it will eat regular laboratory chow. The syndrome, which may last for several months, finally recovers except that the animal *may* show some finickiness and a long-range loss in ability to maintain water balance.

There are several additional points to be considered with aphagia. Very little damage to the lateral hypothalamus is necessary to produce the syndrome. In fact, with some animals, merely lowering an electrode without current is sufficient (Morgane, 1961a, b). Secondly, the less original tissue destroyed, the faster and more complete the recovery (Morgane, 1961c). Finally, once the animal has recovered, additional lesions made in adjacent areas reinstate the syndrome (Teitelbaum and Epstein, 1962).

The lateral hypothalamus thus seems to have effects opposite to those of the ventromedial nucleus, and is apparently a center concerned with the initiation of eating. This conclusion is substantiated by several studies in which the lateral hypothalamus was stimulated either electrically (Wyrwicka et al., 1959) or chemically (Epstein, 1960; Grossman, 1960), resulting in the animal immediately starting to eat available food. Of added interest are the observations that lateral stimulation elicits a previously learned response which in the past had been associated with the receipt of food (e.g., Wyrwicka et al., 1959).

Internal Controls on Lateral Hypothalamus

As with the discussion of the ventromedial "satiation" center, mention should be made of the normal physiological processes that elicit activity in this lateral "feeding" center. On this question, some evidence has been accumulated (see review by Anand, 1961) which points to multiple routes innervating the lateral hypothalamus. Bodily states associated with food depletion such as lowered blood sugar utilization (Anand et al., 1964) have been correlated with altered electrical activity in this hypothalamic area. Indirect evidence relating decreases in brain temperature (e.g., Andersson and Larsson, 1961) to eating suggests also that thermal factors are involved. However, the picture remains tentative at present and must await considerable investigation. Some inconsistent results suggest that issues regarding the precision of recording and data analysis may not be uniform across studies. Grossman and Rechtschaffen (1966), for example, measured hypothalamic temperature at a variety of sites in the cat and found no systematic covariation with eating. Epstein (1960) injected glucose directly into the lateral area and found no changes in food intake. In general, then, inconsistent results await clarification, and it appears that the electrophysiological recording techniques of such investigators as Anand hold great promise for the future.

Dual-center Theory

Taking the experimental work that has been carried out on the hypothalamus as a whole, a picture emerges showing the reciprocal controls on feeding behavior exerted by the ventromedial and the lateral areas. This dual-control theory was first formalized by Anand and Brobeck in 1951 and is still predominant in the field (e.g., see Teitelbaum, 1964). As indicated in the preceding sections, the internal processes which presumably control the activity of these two centers have received considerable attention, but as yet no complete picture has emerged. Theoretically, multiple routes in a complex network have been suggested, all the way from variables associated with food in the stomach, through the mechanisms translating these gastric events into central nervous system changes, to the neural controls on consummatory and learned food-seeking responses.

As can be imagined, the methodological problems in doing this type of research are tremendous and have led to considerable controversy. The production of lesions in small areas of brain tissue inevitably raises a question of precise localization. Indeed, there is some evidence that even the method of producing the lesion may be a factor. Reynolds (1963) compared radio-frequency lesions in the ventromedial nucleus with the more conventional direct-current technique and found that the former produced little hyperphagia or obesity. In addition, in assessing the food-related effects of surgery, the palatability of the foods seems to be a factor in accounting for different findings. Lesions may also produce a host of seemingly secondary, peripheral effects which may well be related to the phenomenon under study. For example, ventromedial lesions and the resulting increased food intake have been associated with varying degrees of structural abnormality of the intestinal walls and kidneys (Brobeck et al., 1943). Lastly, in recording electrical activity in neural structures, there are innumerable problems in delineating artifacts from true experimental effects and in accurately correlating changes in electrical activity with the independent variable (e.g., variations in glucose uptake).

Considering these problems of control and occasionally inconsistent results, the dual-center notion appears to be a reasonable first approximation as a theory. There are, however, still obvious gaps in our knowledge which have to be filled in. For example, the theory does not handle adequately the complexity of behavioral changes which take place following ventromedial and lateral lesions. Neither does it specify the details of the interaction between the two centers. In connection with this latter point, Anand and Brobeck (1951) present data that the lateral area is the more basic since aphagia develops when both the lateral and ventromedial areas are destroyed. Lastly, as pointed out earlier, these centers seem to be parts of a larger neural feeding system. Although some of these other structures have been identified, the experiments outside the hypothalamus have frequently been concerned with other matters and the observations concerning feeding behavior have been incidental. Thus the whole question of the methodological adequacy of these studies needs to be raised, e.g., imprecise electrode placements with no subsequent histological verification, etc. (Erlich, 1964).

FUTURE DIRECTIONS OF RESEARCH

We are thus approaching the end of the story, as far as it is known, with respect to feeding behavior. However, this chapter would not be complete without at least a mention of some of the current work which, as yet, does not neatly dovetail with the existing theories. Hence this concluding section will probably raise more questions than provide new information. The areas to be mentioned include biochemical variables, learning variables, and a reexamination of taste.

Biochemical Variables

The theories and data concerning the chemical constituents of the blood and their effects on the hypothalamus have already been reviewed and, hence, will not be repeated here, except to say that the search for other biochemical transmitters continues. The existence of specific hungers argues for the multiplicity of these sorts of effects in the body. This section is concerned more specifically with some recent work carried out by Neal Miller and associates dealing with the concept of chemical coding in the hypothalamus (Miller, 1965).

Let us begin with some definitions: transmission in the synapses of the parasympathetic nervous system is mediated by a chemical substance called *acetylcholine*. Chemicals having this effect are called *cholinergic*. On the other hand, innervation of most target organs in the sympathetic division of this system is via norepinephrine, and this effect is termed *adrenergic*. Biochemical analyses reveal that the hypothalamus is rich in both acetylcholine and norepinephrine and, moreover, they have rather specific effects.

Grossman (1960) found that introducing norepinephrine into the lateral feeding center of a satiated rat produced eating behavior or a previously learned behavioral response which led to food reinforcement. On the other hand, if a cholinergic chemical was placed in exactly the same location, the behavioral response was drinking or learned water-related responses. Via a long series of control studies it was found that these were not just side effects of some other physiological processes, but the result of direct chemical stimulation of the lateral hypothalamus.

These and other similar data led Miller to raise the possibility of some sort of chemical coding that takes place in the central nervous system. One chemical triggers one particular behavioral system, whereas another chemical applied *to exactly the same cells* elicits another behavioral system. That these are not merely reflexive behaviors is pointed up by the fact that complex, learned behaviors with respect to food or water can be elicited.

Miller then extends this line of reasoning one step further. Perhaps these chemical agents activate a whole homeostatic system—both physiological and behavioral—which regulates the body's utilization and intake of either food or water. If this were the case, adrenergic stimulation of the lateral hypothalamus should produce not only food-seeking behavior but also physiological changes associated with a depleted food supply, e.g., the release of nutritional stores in the liver and fat, resulting in elevated glucose levels in the blood. This is indeed the case as found by Chun-Wuei Chein and Miller (1965). Comparable physiological adjustments occurred with cholinergic stimulation and conservation of water in the body.

The general implications of this work seem relatively clear. Whereas up until now the search for integrating mechanisms in the feeding system has been largely neural (the hypothalamus particularly), we must now also look toward biochemical integrating mechanisms as well. The prospects should keep researchers in the area happy and busy for years to come.

Learning Variables

The use of food-deprived animals in learning experiments has played a major role in laboratory techniques in psychology, and it has been exceptionally important in developing a body of data about the laws of learning. However, relatively little effort has been devoted to the study of how learning principles operate along with physiological processes to regulate food intake. In this section a few suggestive areas of study are listed.

1. Of particular interest has been the growing recognition by American psychologists of the research coming out of the Russian laboratories, stimulated largely by reviews of this work by Razran (1961). The relevant work here is concerned with research on what has been termed *interoceptive conditioning*, i.e., stimuli produced by internal physiological events can serve as conditioned stimuli for either externally observable responses or other internal physiological events. Two such studies are mentioned here to illustrate this approach with respect to food-related behavior.

In one study (Fel'berbaum, 1952) fistulas were surgically prepared in the uteruses of three female dogs so that water at varying temperatures could be passed through this region. Following this preparation, a conditioning procedure was instituted in which the uterus was irrigated with water at 8 to 12°C 10 seconds prior to feeding. After as few as six such pairings of uterine stimulation and food, conditioned salivation and food-related behaviors were elicited by the uterine stimulation alone. Further-more, with added training, the animals could distinguish between the 8 to 12°C water and that at 44 to 48°C. Internal events thus appear to be capable of eliciting, through conditioning, basic feeding behaviors.

In a more complex study (Kassil, 1959) it was noted that salt prefer-ences in dogs decreased after 300 to 500 cc of salt solution were introduced directly into their stomachs via a fistula. This, of course, is not an unex-pected finding. In a subsequent conditioning procedure, however, these salt solutions were preceded by distentions of the dogs' stomachs via a rubber ballon which had been placed there and into which were poured 300 to 500 cc of plain water. After several of these pairings it was found that mere distention of the stomach was enough to produce a decrease in salt preference. Here, then, an internal physical stimulus apparently brought about a conditioned behavioral change in a complex-choice situation.

Although these studies leave several methodological questions unan-swered (e.g., the aversive affects of the stomach balloon bringing about avoidance responses), they raise an interesting possibility: could it be that a wide variety of food-related internal stimuli (e.g., taste, stimuli associated with chewing and swallowing, stomach distention, etc.) be-come naturally occurring conditioned stimuli which elicit activity in the central nervous system? Thus, for example, perhaps the stimulus of a spoonful of food in the mouth has become a conditioned stimulus which brings about some altered activity in the ventromedial nucleus, thereby tending to slow down further eating. Here, then, would be another class of mechanisms, in addition to the physiological ones mentioned earlier, related to controls on intake.

2. Probably the most direct demonstration of a physiological-learning interaction has been in the studies involving lateral hypothalamic stimula-tion mentioned earlier. As a first step in these studies, a food-deprived animal was taught to make a complex behavioral response in order to receive food reinforcement. Following the establishment of this behavior, electrical or chemical stimulation of the lateral feeding center, *even in satiated animals*, elicited the previously learned behavioral response. This phenomenon has been demonstrated in a variety of situations: rats push-ing on a hinged door (Coons and Miller, 1957); rats pressing a bar in a Skinner box (Grossman, 1960); rats running across an electrified grid (Morgane, 1961c), and goats placing a foreleg on the food tray (Wyr-wicka and Dobrzecka, 1960). Furthermore, these last investigators also were able to produce an inhibition of the learned response via ventro-medial stimulation, pointing again to the reciprocal effects of these two centers.

3. A related series of studies is of potential importance in understanding the relationships between learning and physiological processes—the work of Olds on the reinforcing effects of electrical self-stimulation. In the classic study, Olds and Milner (1954) implanted electrodes in various parts of the rat brain. They then arranged the apparatus so that, when the rat made a designated behavioral response (pressing a bar), the only stimulation received was a small electric current through the implanted electrode. For certain electrode placements it was found that the rats showed a very high bar-press rate, receiving only this intracranial stimulation as a consequence of their behavior. In subsequent investigations relatively few of these "reinforcement" areas of the brain were found (notably in the limbic system), but of particular importance for the present discussion were the findings that many of these reinforcement centers and areas of the brain that elicit feeding responses when stimulated tend to be one and the same. This is particularly true of the lateral hypothalamus (Margules and Olds, 1962).

Here, then, we have a neurological tie-in between one of the great homeostatic systems of the body and an equally important set of psychological concepts: those of reinforcement, reward, appetite, or whatever term different theorists have used to describe seemingly pleasurable experience. Two levels of discourse thus find a common meeting ground in a small area of the brain. These issues will be elaborated in Chapter VIII, but for the moment this area of investigation seems to be a fruitful approach toward a reanalysis of the role of taste and taste-mediated food preferences in the regulation of intake.

A Reexamination of Taste

It will be recalled that in an earlier discussion the experimental evidence indicated that taste factors do play a role in regulating intake, but, as yet, no physiological mechanisms had been discovered indicating by what means this control takes place. It seemed apparent that utilizing the term *preference* or any other term denoting pleasurable taste did not really explain the phenomena involved. As a look to the future, however, perhaps some speculation is in order.

Olds' work on the electrical self-stimulation certainly gives the concept of reinforcement a neurological base and relates this whole area to emotional behavior in general (see Chapter VIII). As has already been pointed out, many of these reinforcement areas also largely correspond with "feeding" areas, thus providing a strong physiological connection between the two systems. The missing link here seems to be a connection between the classical medullary-thalamic-cortical taste pathway and the aforementioned areas of the limbic-hypothalamic system concerned with emotions and feeding. If such collaterals from the classical pathway could be discovered, as Pfaffman (1961) suggests, then we would have the groundwork established for the study of the physiological-emotional basis of taste preferences. Perhaps one of the current readers of this book will continue this important line of investigation.

SUMMARY

Organisms display an amazing ability to regulate their food intake so as to maintain a constant internal environment. This process seems to be mediated by incompletely understood taste factors as well as more fully delineated postingestion events. The key to the process, as now understood, is in the multiple effects of (a) biochemical changes in the blood; (b) alterations in the distention of the stomach and, very likely, gastric motility; and (c) temperature changes that are associated with depletion or ingestion. Each of these classes of events has presumed effects on the electrical activity of two rather small portions of the hypothalamus—the lateral and the ventromedial areas. These areas, in turn, are primary structures mediating the initiation and inhibition of complex, learned feeding behaviors, and as such have been termed the *feeding* and the *satiation* areas of the brain.

Topics of potential interest in the field for future research include (a) the more complex effects of interoceptive conditioning and learning in general on food regulation; (b) the neurological substrate mediating taste-related preferences and the relationship between reinforcement, taste, and intake; and (c) the search for specific biochemical agents as controllers of eating behaviors.

IV

Behavior Related to Water and Drinking

The maintenance of water balance is a most critical set of operations for the organism. Failure to take in adequate amounts of water over a prolonged period of time produces dangerous alterations in physiological processes (e.g., a rise in body temperature), which eventually become lethal. A physically fit man lost in the hot desert, for example, would be dead in less than 36 hours without water. Thus, as with the topic of hunger, the regulation of water intake is one of the vital bodily functions, and since drinking is the only way that water is normally taken in, this area of study again represents a meeting ground of behavior and physiology.

Water is normally lost from the body through three main routes: (*a*) evaporation in the respiratory system; (*b*) perspiration; and (*c*) the elimination of urine and feces, with sweating and urine excretion representing the main avenues of loss. Water intake, on the other hand, has only one usual route, and that is through drinking or ingesting food with water content. The physiological-behavioral mechanisms which maintain the delicate balance between water loss and water ingestion are the subject matter of this chapter.

Before proceeding, some of the mechanics of water absorption by the body need to be reviewed. In the adult human, approximately 70% of the body weight is water. The water is distributed throughout the body in the following areas: within the cells (intracellular fluid); in the blood and lymphatic systems (intravascular fluid); and in the spaces between cells (interstitial fluid).

After water is ingested, it passes through the stomach relatively quickly and is normally absorbed into the blood stream in the upper part of the small intestine. The rate of absorption, however, is dependent primarily on the ion concentration (osmotic pressure) of the water relative to that of the plasma in the bloodstream. If, for example, the ingested water has a high concentration of salt in it, thus making its *tonicity* higher than that of the plasma, a rather unusual phenomenon occurs. Rather than water being absorbed into the blood stream, water flows from the blood into the intestine until the tonicity of the water in the intestine is equal to that of the plasma. Thus this *hypertonic* solution has the effect of pulling water out of the vascular system until the plasma and the water in the gut are *isotonic*.

With ingested solutions, the ion concentration of which is less than that of the plasma (i.e., *hypotonic* solutions), the reverse process occurs. Water flows from the intestine into the blood stream until isotonicity occurs. Naturally, the lower the tonicity of the solution, the faster the absorption into the blood stream, with pure water being absorbed most rapidly.

There is a second stage to this process of water transport. Once water is absorbed into the blood stream, it is carried to cells in all the tissues of the body. Here, again, the tonicity of the plasma relative to that of the tissue cells appears to be critical. When the concentration of the ions in the plasma is increased, for example, under water deprivation or with salt injection, water flows from the cells into the plasma, thus bringing about *cellular dehydration*. By the same process water is made available to the tissue cells when conditions are reversed. As will be shown later, these changes in osmotic pressure, particularly in certain cells of the central nervous system, appear to be exceptionally important neural triggers for bringing about water balance. In actuality we are dealing here with *effective osmotic pressure*, a portion of total osmotic pressure in a system which regulates the amount of solvent that will pass across a membrane when there are unequal concentrations of a solute on either side of the membrane.

Gilman (1937) and Holmes and Gregerson (1950) demonstrated that the relevant variable in thirst-motivated behavior was not the concentration of solute per se but effective osmotic pressure. Intravenous injections of sodium chloride, which does not readily pass through cell membranes, produced decreases in cell volume and was associated with the drinking of large amounts of water. Intravenous administration of urea, adjusted to produce increases in osmotic pressure comparable to that of the sodium chloride (but which does pass through cell membranes) had only a small effect on subsequent drinking. Thus it appears that the *difference* in concentration between cells and plasma produced by sodium chloride, resulting in fluid transport from cells to the plasma (with resultant cellular dehydration), was the effective process in the initiation of drinking.

PHYSIOLOGICAL ADJUSTMENTS TO WATER DEFICIT

Before the controls on water intake can be meaningfully discussed, a review of the major physiological changes which occur during water deficit is necessary. When an organism is deprived of water, a variety of physical adjustments takes place, some of which tend to conserve water in the body. As will be seen, however, these physiological attempts to maintain water balance occasionally take place at the expense of other bodily systems.

Oral Changes

As stated earlier, under water deprivation the osmotic pressures (ion concentration) of the blood increases, which, in turn, draws water from the cells of the body. A particularly important group of cells which thus become dehydrated are those in the mouth region and those associated with the production of saliva. In the early theorizing on this topic, dryness of the mouth was thought to be the primary stimulus concerning the experience of thirst and, hence, exerted major control over drinking behavior (Cannon, 1932). In light of all the more recent work on thirst, however, it becomes apparent that this oral factor is only one of a large number of processes associated with deprivation.

Perspiration

With prolonged water deprivation, there is also a decrease in the amount of water lost via sweating, thus reducing the rate at which the body is becoming dehydrated (Grande et al., 1957). However, the evaporation of sweat from the skin surface is a major source of body cooling in hot environments and during physical work. The reduction in sweating during dehydration is thus upsetting one of the factors involved in thermoregulation, and a rise in body temperature will occur. This increase in temperature appears to be a linear function of the cumulative body water deficit (Grande et al., 1957). To take a relatively extreme example, water deprivation in a hot environment, with moderate physical work being performed, will result in a body temperature of over 102° F after 4 hours of these conditions. This is associated with approximately a 50% reduction in sweat production. It seems apparent, then, that water and temperature regulations are intimately connected with each other via the mechanism of sweat production. As will be shown later in the discussion of the central nervous system, there is also good evidence of a linkage between drinking and thermoregulatory areas of the hypothalamus.

Antidiuretic Hormone

The role of the antidiuretic hormone (ADH) in water balance is still being investigated, although several facts about its operation are well established. It is produced in neurosecretory cells in the hypothalamus (supraoptic area), with increases in its production occurring during periods of water deficit. This increased secretion is most likely elicited by changes in the cellular hydration of portions of the hypothalamus (Andersson and McCann, 1955).

The primary function of ADH is to reduce the loss of body water through the urine. This is accomplished by its bringing about an increased reabsorption of water in the tubules of the kidneys. Thus prolonged water deprivation elicits the secretion of antidiuretic hormone into the blood stream, which, in turn, produces a decrease in the amount and an increase in the concentration of urine excreted. Damage to the posterior pituitary or the associated hypothalamic areas produces a syndrome known as *diabetes insipidus,* excessive loss of water via the kidneys and urine. The symptoms are characterized by chronic feelings of thirst and excessive drinking (polydipsia) as well as excessive urination (polyuria), thus highlighting the important role played by ADH in maintaining water balance. A discussion of the physiological processes that trigger the secretion of ADH will be reserved for a later portion of the chapter.

More recent evidence points to some secondary effects of ADH. The presence of this hormone in the bloodstream also seems to decrease the volume and to increase the concentration of saliva, thus implicating it possibly in oral sensations related to the experience of thirst. ADH also seems to promote the absorption of water from the gut into the bloodstream (Towbin, 1964). Hence it may play an even more general and important role in maintaining water balance than previously suspected.

VARIABLES ASSOCIATED WITH THE GASTROINTESTINAL TRACT

As with the discussion of the controls on eating, the following section reviews the role played by oral-gastric factors in the regulation of water intake. In a later portion of the chapter, these peripheral events will be related to processes occurring in the central nervous system.

Oral Metering

There is reasonable evidence that, in some species, oral stimuli associated with the act of drinking participate in the regulation of the amount ingested. In an early and well-known study by Adolph (1939) dogs were water-deprived for varying lengths of time by maintaining them on dry diets. When the dogs were then given access to water at the end of the deprivation period, the amount of water drunk was, on the average, equal to the accumulated body water deficit. Moreover, this drinking to satiation occurred in a few minutes, ending long before the water had reached any body tissue where it was to be deposited. Thus there is preliminary evidence here of some immediate metering of intake in the oral-gastric system which takes place before tissue needs are met.

In another study dogs were prepared with esophageal fistulas so that ingested water would pour out before reaching the stomach. Dogs in water deficit now drank *in proportion* to the accumulated deficit, but over-all drank about twice as much to reach temporary satiation (Bellows and Van Wagenen, 1938). Here, then, is further evidence for the operation of an oral factor, because the animals drank in proportion to their deficits. As might be expected, however, the temporary satiation achieved under these conditions was short-lived because the bodily water deficits were not being replenished. The animals became restless relatively quickly and would again start drinking. It is obvious, then, that oral metering is only one part of a larger and more complex set of controls on intake.

Gastric Metering

In the discussion on the "stop" factors in eating (Chapter III), it will be recalled that stomach distention played an important role. This same process seems to occur with drinking as well. We have already seen how dogs have the ability to drink very quickly and accurately the right amount of water to make up a body deficit. If, however, their stomachs are artificially distended by inflating a rubber balloon which had previously been inserted, the amount of water intake drops proportionally to the amount of distention (Towbin, 1949). Thus, again, the stretch receptors in the walls of the stomach and their connections with the brain via the vagus nerve serve an important function in inhibiting further ingestion when the stomach is getting full.

Other evidence of the inhibitory role played by stomach distention is provided in a study by O'Kelley and Falk (1958). During the critical portion of this experiment, rats were deprived of water for 23.5 hours and then allowed to press a bar in order to obtain small drinks of water during a half-hour test period. Naturally, the faster the bar-pressing rate, the more water became available for the rat to drink. Shortly before the bar pressing was to begin various volumes of water were placed directly (through a fistula) into the rats' stomachs. These investigators found that the larger the volume of the stomach preload, the lower was the number of bar presses for water during the test period.

Under normal circumstances, then, both oral and gastric processes seem to play important roles in regulating water intake. Dry tissues in the mouth and reduced salivary output appear to be oral factors related to the initiation of drinking. The mouth, through some as yet unidentified process, also plays an inhibitory role in that it seems partially to meter how much water has been taken in and is thus related to the cessation of drinking. Similarly, stomach distention is involved as a "stop" factor, signaling to the organism that satiation is being reached.

Species Differences

As already indicated, dogs who have been water deprived drink to satiation with great speed and then stop. Since this ingestion pattern typically occurs before the body cells have received water, it appears that the dog has a very sensitive oral-gastric metering system which can estimate the body's water needs. This same mode of drinking occurs with burrows, camels, and young rabbits. On the other hand, rodents, adult rabbits, and man drink much more slowly. They also frequently need a food supplement or liquids in a palatable form in order to make up completely a water deficit. For example, in a hot, industrial situation, workers do not usually drink enough water to compensate for that lost through sweat during working hours. Even if water is readily available and is provided at an appropriately cool temperature, this voluntary dehydration is more the rule than the exception. The water deficit is, of course, eventually made up after working hours when perhaps liquids in more pleasant form are available (Henschel, 1964). What the anatomical differences are that could account for these varied drinking patterns have not yet been worked out. Needless to say, however, these species differences make generalizations about controls on intake difficult.

Taste Factors

Zotterman and his associates in Sweden have, for many years, been studying the electrical activity in the taste nerves coming from the tongue. Of particular interest here is their finding of increased discharge in some of these neural fibers when the tongue is irrigated with pure water. Using extensive control procedures, these investigators were able to rule out the possibility that the electrical activity was produced by touch or thermal receptors in the tongue, thus suggesting that some species might actually be able to "taste" pure water (e.g., Cohen et al., 1955).

These electrophysiological results have been obtained with dogs, cats, pigs, rabbits, and monkeys. The only species that do not show this electrical response to pure water, that have been thus far studied, are man and the rat. It is interesting that dogs, for example, who seem to be capable of sensitive oral metering of intake, have been found to possess these water taste fibers; whereas man and the rat, who replenish water deficits relatively slowly, show no evidence of these types of fibers (Towbin, 1964). Admittedly this is speculative at this point, and a great deal of anatomical-behavioral investigation will be needed to clarify the role of taste in water regulation.

INTAKE VARIABLES ASSOCIATED WITH OSMOTIC PRESSURE

In the preceding section the role of the gastrointestinal tract was discussed, with emphasis on its responsiveness to the *volume* of water taken in. In this section the primary focus is on the *osmotic pressure* of the solution ingested. To begin with, let us review the effects of ingested *hypertonic* salt solutions on the plasma and the body cells. It will be recalled that, under this condition, water is pulled from the plasma into the intestine. This increases the osmotic pressure of the plasma, which, in turn, leads to cellular dehydration and the experience of thirst. In this portion of the chapter, a closer look at this *salt-induced thirst* will be taken.

One part of the previously cited O'Kelley and Falk (1958) study is relevant here. Rats had been water deprived for 23.5 hours and then had to press a bar to receive small drinks of water during the half-hour test period. In the earlier description of this study, the effects of different volumes of water in a stomach preload were discussed. In a second part of the experiment, the volume of the preload was held constant but it varied in salt concentration. The question now being asked was how the osmotic pressure of the solution in the gut affected subsequent bar pressing for water.

The results were as expected. The salt concentration of plasma in the rat is approximately 0.87%. When the concentration of the preloaded stomach solution was higher than this, the rats showed greater subsequent bar pressing and drinking of pure water than did control animals with no preload. When the concentration of the stomach load was 0.87%, thus making it isotonic for the rat, the amount of subsequent drinking was very slightly less than that of the control animals, i.e., it was as if practically no preload had been introduced. Finally, when the concentration of the stomach load was less than 0.87% (hypotonic), the amount of water subsequently ingested was less than that of the control animals. These results are depicted in Figure 4.1. It thus appears that effective osmotic pressure is the critical variable in this situation. With hypertonic loads in the gut pulling water out of the plasma and ultimately producing cellular dehydration, the rat drank more water. With a hypotonic solution

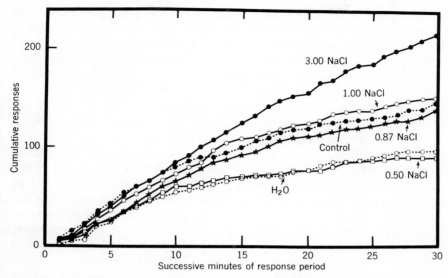

Figure 4.1 Bar pressing for water in rats whose stomach preload varied in salt concentration. Note that the response level for the isotonic group (0.87%) is somewhat below that of the control animals, probably indicating that the volume of the preload is having some effect on intake. [*Courtesy of O'Kelley and Falk (1958).*]

in the gut, thereby pushing water into the plasma and cells, the rat reduced his drinking.

This maintenance of a constant salt concentration in the blood was also found by Stellar et al. (1954), who used much the same techniques. Of added interest in this study was the use of an esophageal fistula with several of their rats who were given no preloads and were not deprived. Here, of course, the rats drink (taste) a solution which never reaches the stomach, since it is removed through the fistula in the esophagus. They found that the rats drank the greatest amount when the concentration of the solution was 0.87%. This not only supports the results cited previously but also suggests that a taste factor plays a role in maintaining the salt constancy in the body.

Summary of Physiological and Behavioral Adjustments

Before proceeding to a discussion of the events in the central nervous system which underlie the processes described thus far, a summary is in order.

When the body is deprived of water, a number of physiological changes take place: the plasma draws water from the cells, bringing about cellular dehydration and increasing the cellular osmotic pressure; the production of sweat is decreased, thus slowing the rate of water loss from this avenue, but at the expense of thermal regulation; antidiuretic hormone is secreted into the blood stream which reduces water loss via the kidneys and promotes the absorption of water in the gut.

With respect to behavior, there seem to be two immediate "start" factors which initiate drinking responses: dry tissues in the mouth and the osmotic pressure of the extracellular fluid going above some "normal" level. The higher the tonicity of the plasma, for example, thus leading to cellular dehydration, the greater the volume of water ingested. Thermal factors also play a role here. There is also evidence of a variety of "stop" factors which seem to bring about a cessation of drinking when the body's water deficit has been replenished. These include oral metering in some species, possibly related to taste; stomach distention; the osmotic pressure of the extracellular fluid going below some "normal" level; and thermal factors.

As can be seen, then, there is a complex physiological-behavioral series of events continually in operation tending to keep the organism's state of hydration at some constant level. The processes in the central nervous system which coordinate all these adjustments are the subject of the next portion of this chapter.

VARIABLES ASSOCIATED WITH THE CENTRAL NERVOUS SYSTEM

The reader will recall in Chapter III that most of the experimental work concerning the neural controls on eating were centered in the hypothalamus. The same is true for thirst. Although some research has touched on areas other than the hypothalamus, these, for the moment, appear to be secondary and, hence, will not be covered (Morgane, 1964). It appears that the hypothalamic influences on thirst mechanisms are less well understood than those related to hunger. The complexity of the situation is increased by the fact that thirst is so intimately bound up with other physiological systems, notably thermoregulation, hormonal output (ADH), blood chemistry, and, of course, hunger itself. Thus, to keep the picture in the central nervous system relatively clear, the various subtopics will be discussed separately to be followed by an integrating summary in the section on the lateral hypothalamus.

Thermoregulation and Thirst

The interrelationship between these two regulatory systems has already been touched upon in connection with sweat production. Now a far more direct interaction between the two in the hypothalamus will be reviewed. The preoptic-anterior area of the hypothalamus (see Figure A.3) was implicated as the site involved in thermal regulation in the classic experiments of Magoun et al., (1938) (see Chapter V). It was thought that the area contained neural cells which are responsive to changes in body temperature; i.e., cells in this region will show altered electrical activity as the body temperature deviates from normal. More recently, Hardy and his associates (Nakayama et al., 1961) have substantiated this view by inserting recording microelectrodes into this area and measuring changes in electrical activity in response to alterations of temperature. The most relevant work for purposes of this chapter, however, has been the very fascinating experiments by Bengt Andersson in Stockholm (Andersson et al., 1964).

Andersson utilized some interesting techniques for actually warming or cooling this small thermoregulatory area of the hypothalamus. Cooling was accomplished by having a permanently implanted thermode (very finely drawn tubing through which water at various temperatures can be perfused) placed in the preoptic-anterior region of goats. Included in the implant was a thermosensitive recording device to verify the temperature being produced. This same apparatus could be used for local warming of the hypothalamus, but it was found that a more precise effect could be obtained by inserting two tiny parallel plates into the region which could produce radio-frequency heating between them.

Upon local heating of the preoptic-anterior area, Andersson found a whole range of physiological-behavioral changes, all involving adjustments concerned with maintaining a constant body temperature: increased panting (the counterpart of sweating), dilation of the blood vessels, an inhibition of shivering, a decrease in food intake, and, most important for the current discussion, an *increase in water intake*. Furthermore, this increase in drinking did not appear to be just a reflex act, but a series of well-coordinated drinking behaviors which were no different than the normal water ingestion which occurs in a hot environment. Thus it appears that there are heat-sensitive cells in this region of the hypothalamus which exert some form of control over patterned drinking (and eating) behaviors as well as serving to activate physiological "heat loss" mechanisms.

As might have been anticipated, the opposite effects were obtained when the preoptic-anterior area was cooled. The major changes were increased shivering, vasoconstriction, increased secretion of norepinephrine and epinephrine, increased food consumption, and *decreased water intake*.

Several interesting additional points should be brought out here.

1. In a cold environment there is an increased caloric need in the body; hence, the increased eating noted previously fits in nicely as a thermo-regulatory mechanism. The opposite is true, of course, in a hot environment, where additional calories via food intake would work against thermal regulation. Thus Andersson's finding of a decrease in food consumption when the hypothalamus is warmed also makes physiological sense.

2. The secretion of the adrenergic substances, norepinephrine and epinephrine, during local cooling is particularly interesting in view of the biochemical coding which apparently takes place in the hypothalamus. It will be recalled, from the previous chapter, that reference was made to the work of Grossman (1960) in which he found that adrenergic stimulation of the lateral hypothalamus brought about eating behavior, whereas cholinergic (acetylcholine) stimulation to the same cells produced drinking behavior. Here, then, is at least partial evidence of a hormonal connection between thermoregulation (the secretion of epinephrine and norepinephrine when the preoptic-anterior area is cooled) and eating behavior (the elicitation of feeding responses when these adrenergic substances circulating in the blood stream reach the lateral hypothalamus).

Summary. Water intake plays an important role in thermal regulation, with drinking going up when the body temperature increases (along with other heat loss mechanisms) and going down when the temperature decreases. These effects seem to be mediated by the preoptic-anterior area of the hypothalamus which contains cells that are sensitive to changes in body temperature. The exact method by which this area of the hypothalamus controls drinking behavior is yet to be found: processes in the preoptic-anterior area may directly trigger a more basic "drinking center" in the lateral hypothalamus (to be discussed later), or hormonal secretions may be produced which then exert specific influences in a basic "drinking center." For the time being, all we can do is marvel at the exquisite complexity of the body's regulatory systems.

Antidiuretic Hormone and Thirst

The role of ADH in the conservation of body water has already been discussed, along with a brief description of its origin in the supraoptic-pituitary axis. A question remains, however, concerning the hypothalamic mechanisms which bring about the secretion of ADH into the blood stream during periods of water deficit. Again we are indebted to Andersson and his colleagues for the major experimental work.

The most likely hypothesis concerning the neural triggering of ADH is that there are certain areas of the hypothalamus which are sensitive to changes in osmotic pressure. Thus, when the plasma pulls water from body cells (including these hypothalamic cells) during water deficit, the electrical activity in these neural areas is changed, thereby eliciting the secretion of ADH. This hypothesis received strong support from Andersson's research wherein he injected small volumes of hypertonic salt solutions directly into various portions of the hypothalamus (1953). Increasing the osmotic pressure in this way in certain cells of the hypothalamus brought about an increase in both ADH secretion and drinking behavior in goats. The physiological-behavioral response was just as if a sharp water deficit had been produced in the animals. Injection of iso- or hypotonic salt solutions, on the other hand, had no affect on either ADH secretion or drinking behavior.

Since this early experimentation considerable effort has gone into "mapping" the areas of the hypothalamus that are sensitive to changes in osmotic pressure. As might be expected, the supraoptic area was found to be one such region. A more detailed description of these osmoreceptor areas is beyond the scope of this chapter (Andersson and McCann, 1955); however, several interesting aspects of this later work should be mentioned. Some osmosensitive regions, when infused with hypertonic solutions, produced only ADH secretion but no drinking behavior; other sites produced drinking but no ADH effects; and others elicited both (e.g., supraoptic area). The implication of these findings is that changes in osmotic pressure present a highly critical stimulus for the elicitation of a complex regulatory subsystem, involving both hormonal-renal (kidney) mechanisms and behavioral responses to take in water.

To keep the role of the hypothalamus in focus, a brief summary is in order. There is evidence that both thermoreceptors and osmoreceptors in the hypothalamus play important roles in water balance. The former are involved in physiological temperature-control mechanisms as well as complex drinking behaviors. The latter are implicated in physiological water-conservation processes and, again, complex drinking behaviors. A question which is as yet unanswered in the field is whether the hypothalamic areas containing these receptors exert *direct* control over drinking behavior, or whether they merely influence another, more primary, "drinking area," which, in turn, controls behavior. Preliminary evidence seems to favor the second alternative in that the thermo- and osmosensitive areas (and several others) send out neural fiber systems which funnel through the lateral hypothalamus.

Lateral Hypothalamus

It will be recalled that the work of Teitelbaum (1961) cited in Chapter III revealed that surgical destruction of the lateral hypothalamic area in rats produced both aphagia (inability to eat) and adipsia (inability to drink). This section takes a closer look at this and subsequent research, with particular emphasis on the drinking deficit. A major technological problem in studying the loss of water-related behavior in these animals is, of course, that they are dying of starvation. The development of special feeding techniques, however, by Teitelbaum and his co-workers keep the animals alive so that they eventually regain normal eating behaviors. Long-range drinking deficits can now be studied in these "recovered" animals.

Using such "recovered laterals," Epstein and Teitelbaum (1964) found that the rats had far from recovered in their drinking behavior, even though food-related behavior appeared normal. Their results can be summarized as follows:

1. A substantial number of rats remained permanently adipsic.
2. Those that did regain some drinking behavior did not increase their drinking in response to water deprivation the way normals do.
3. They did not drink when the osmotic pressure of the plasma was increased the way normals do.
4. They do not increase drinking to regulate body temperature in the heat as do normals.
5. The only time they drink at all is while they are eating dry food.

Thus these investigators point out that the animals do not display any of the drinking processes which are normally regulatory in nature. It is just as if a central relay station in a complex communications network were not functioning, so that signals from the thermosensitive and osmosensitive areas of the hypothalamus could not be received. The only stimulus which elicited drinking was the rather peripheral one of a dry mouth. These results suggest that the lateral hypothalamus, being a site for the convergence of many fiber pathways, plays a central coordinating role in the elicitation of drinking behavior.

Other Mechanisms

The view that water intake is regulated by osmotic and thermal mechanisms in the central nervous system is certainly a generally accepted one, but by no means are the issues beyond controversy. There is reasonable evidence, for example, that *overhydration* of cells also can produce sensations of thirst and increased drinking. Holmes and Cizek (1951), among others, found that dogs who were made salt-deficient via extraction procedures and a low-salt diet (thereby producing cellular overhydration) showed marked increases in drinking. This increased consumption returned to normal levels upon restoration of sodium chloride. This finding correlates with observations of clinical patients who are salt-deficient in that they report sensations of thirst which are apparently unaltered by drinking.

The implications of this type of finding with regard to the central-nervous-system mechanisms are somewhat disquieting. It may be, for example, that *changes* in osmotic pressure (Adolph, 1921) or alterations in cellular size (Wolf, 1950) are the critical events in the body's detection of water imbalance. Gilbert and Glaser (1961) suggest that both osmo- and volume-detectors may be present in the central nervous system which interact in the regulation of body water. As yet, however, these tentative notions must await considerable investigation.

LEARNING VARIABLES

As with the area of hunger, there have been a paucity of studies investigating the role of learning in the physiological processes involved in water regulation. The observation that various forms of stimulation of the hypothalamus can elicit previously learned, patterned water-seeking behaviors has already been mentioned and will not be repeated here.

Of more interest is a series of studies by Falk (1964) in which he has been able to induce excessive drinking (polydipsia) in rats without apparently altering any physiological processes or structures. This investigator placed food-deprived rats in a Skinner box in which they had to press a bar in order to get food pellets. Free access to water was provided at all times in the box. When food pellets were delivered at variable intervals of time (variable-interval schedule), he found that the rats' water consumption increased approximately three to five times above normal. The rat would press the bar for a period of time until the food pellet was delivered; then they would eat the pellet and then drink water before returning to the bar to begin pressing again. An explanation for this phenomenon has not yet appeared, although it seems entirely likely that in some way the drinking response in this case, as with any other behavior, is under the control of some external reinforcer. The very fascinating study of the relationship between physiological-regulatory drinking and reinforced learned drinking patterns is just coming under study in a number of laboratories (Schaeffer and Diehl, 1965).

SUMMARY

An organism in water deficit undergoes a variety of physiological-behavioral changes which have the net effect of conserving or restoring body water. These include ADH production, decreased water loss via urine, decreased sweating, transport of body water from cells to the plasma, and, behaviorally, a decrease in (dry) food intake as well as an increase in drinking or learned water-related behaviors. A complex set of sensors in the body seems to signal the status of the organism's water balance. Of these, osmotic and thermal signals seem to be critical, with such systems as oral metering, stomach distention, and dry tissues in the mouth also playing a role. There is reasonable evidence that these signals are channeled through the hypothalamus (to be detected by osmo-, thermo-, and, of course electrosensitive cells). This structure, then, seems to play a coordinating role in initiating both the physiological and behavioral responses designed to restore water balance.

V

Behavior Related to
Temperature Regulation

The human body displays a remarkable ability to maintain a constant internal temperature of 37°C (98.6°F). There are, of course, cyclical changes in this internal temperature which are regular and predictable, such as alterations that occur during sleep or during portions of the female menstrual cycle. However, this relative stability is maintained despite wide fluctuations in temperature, at rest, during exercise, and under a variety of other constantly changing circumstances. This feat is accomplished via two general systems of responses: (*a*) automatic physiological heat-dissipating or heat-conservation mechanisms and (*b*) intelligent, learned behaviors. The former represent the more sensitive and precise set of processes for thermoregulation, whereas the latter, encompassing the whole range of man's ingenuity and engineering skill, allow adjustment to the most extreme thermal environments.

The thermodynamics involved can be viewed at their simplest level in the following terms: body heat is supplied basically as a by-product of the body's metabolic processes. Thus factors such as increased activity, the intake of food, or the production of hormones which step up the organism's metabolism rate all serve to increase body heat. On the other hand, body heat is lost via three principal methods: (*a*) *conduction* through tissue from the interior to the skin surface; (*b*) via *convective* action in the blood stream, as warm blood from the interior is circulated through the cooler surface tissues; and (*c*) directly by *radiation* from the skin surface to the cooler surround. A negligible amount of heat is also lost through vaporization in the respiratory system.

The fact that heat is transferred from warmer to cooler areas is a basic law of thermodynamics. Thus in a cold environment there is heat loss from the body, necessitating physiological and behavioral adjustments to maintain a constant body temperature. Similarly, in hot surroundings the reverse process occurs, with physiological and behavioral heat-dissipating mechanisms preserving constancy.

This sort of temperature regulation has often been likened to the action of an ordinary house thermostat (e.g., Hardy, 1960; Benzinger, 1961a). The components of such a servomechanism can be divided into three general categories: (a) a sensory system; (b) a controller; and, (c) effector mechanisms. In the typical heating and cooling arrangement of a house, the sensory instrument is a thermometer which measures the room temperature. This information is transmitted to a controller which compares the measured temperature with a "set point" temperature at which the occupants want their home maintained. When the measured temperature deviates from the set point, the controller activates the effector mechanisms (either the heating or cooling systems) which then operate until the temperature returns to the desired level.

The purpose of this chapter is to identify and describe the sensor, effector, and controller systems that operate in living organisms to maintain the same sort of internal thermal constancy.

SENSORY SYSTEMS

Controversy concerning the identification of the sensors which detect thermal stimuli has existed for many years. Early research, based largely on the morphological study of the nerve endings in the skin, has given way to direct electrophysiological recordings of peripheral nerve impulses. In addition, the development of precise methods to heat or cool directly certain parts of the hypothalamus has focused attention on this structure as a *thermal receptor* (in addition to its role as part of the controller system). In this section a closer look will be taken at both the sensors in the skin and in the central nervous system as they relate to thermoregulatory processes.

Skin Temperature and Comfort

The classic studies on subjective feelings of comfort at various temperatures were carried out quite early (Houghten et al., 1929; Winslow et al., 1937). Here it was found that a vote of "pleasant" was most often obtained at *skin* temperatures of 33.5°C (92.3°F). There was a sharp change from "pleasant" to "very unpleasant" with a 2.5°C increase in skin temperature. On the other hand, a drop of 4.5°C in skin temperature was required in order to get comparable discomfort judgments on the cold side. At the extremes, thermal pain from cold was elicited at 18°C (64.4°F) and from heat at 45°C (113°F) (Hardy et al., 1952). On the basis of these data, Hardy (1960) suggests that the average skin temperature in humans has a set point around 33.5°C and that deviations from this point evoke thermo-regulatory responses.

Humans are very sensitive to changes in skin temperature. If adapted to a thermally neutral environment, a subject can detect an increase of 0.007°C in skin temperature, whereas it takes a 0.012°C drop in skin temperature to be detected as a change in the cool direction. Differences of these small magnitudes are effective if they occur within a three-second period (Belding et al., 1948). These threshold measurements have been found to vary according to such factors as adapting temperature, body area stimulated, age of subject, etc., and are included here merely to illustrate the high sensitivity of the skin to thermal stimuli.

Specialized Sensory Organs in the Skin

Given the aforementioned facts relating skin temperature to threshold measurements and to feelings of comfort and discomfort, the question arises as to the actual elements in the skin which "sense" the thermal stimuli. For over 40 years a theory proposed by Von Frey in 1895 pre-dominated in the field. This view maintained that there were specialized nerve endings in the skin, each being responsive to one type of stimulus. Thus one type of nerve ending (Krause end bulb) was supposed to sub-serve cold stimulation; Ruffini endings were presumably sensitive to warmth; and free nerve endings were related to painful stimulation. More recent work, however, by Weddell (1954, 1955), who used improved methods to study the structure of the terminations in the skin, has shown that the previously hypothesized special nerve endings were artifactual, and that free nerve endings alone are the relevant structures. Thus it ap-pears that differences in the terminals of the nerves themselves cannot account for the variations in thermal sensation that one experiences.

Electrophysiological Recordings from Peripheral Nerves

The fact that the nerve endings in the skin are morphologically the same, however, should not be taken to mean that they all serve the same function. To the contrary, studies by Hensel and Zotterman (1951), in which they recorded the electric impulses in peripheral nerves of cats, have identified at least three major types of receptor fibers. One only responds to temperature increases; a second type, to a temperature de-crease; and lastly, fibers which are responsive to pressure and marked heating (pain fibers).

Figure 5.1, adapted from Hardy (1960), illustrates the rate of firing in such "cold" and "warm" fibers as a function of skin temperature in the cat. Of importance is the fact that the two curves cross at about the point of thermal neutrality for the cat. Hardy hypothesizes that the skin tempera-

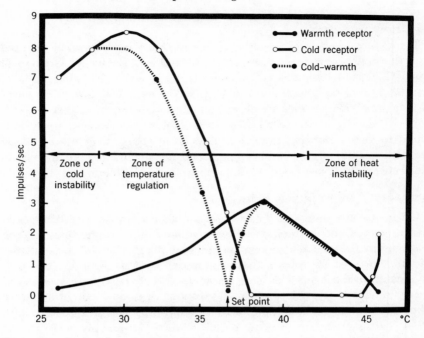

Figure 5.1   Rate of firing in "warm" and "cold" fibers as a function of skin temperature in the cat. [*Adapted from Hardy (1960).*]

ture at which these two types of fibers are firing equally determines the
organism's set point for skin temperature. Considerably more research,
however, is required to substantiate this interesting notion.

Vascular Theory of Thermal Sensation

As yet we have not identified the actual site in the skin where thermal
stimuli are translated into nervous system impulses. Perhaps the leading
theory at the present time concerning this point has been proposed by
Kenshalo and Nafe (1962). These investigators argue against the notion
that certain nerve fibers in the skin are *directly* sensitive to warming and
cooling. They suggest rather that thermal sensation is a function of the
type of tissue in which the free nerve endings are imbedded. The most
likely site of thermal reception, according to the theory, is in the smooth
muscles of the cutaneous (skin) vascular system.

These muscles in the walls of the surface blood vessels are particularly
sensitive to thermal changes—dilating when warmed and constricting
when cooled. Kenshalo and Nafe theorize that it is the resultant mechan-

ical stimulation of the free nerve endings imbedded in these smooth muscles which is the critical stimulus for electric discharge of the nerve. Thus these muscles serve as a "thermomechanical transducer" of thermal energy into electric energy. To date, this theory seems to be the most plausible in terms of incorporating the known facts.

Thermal Receptors in the Hypothalamus

In a series of investigations Benzinger (1959, 1960, 1961b, 1963) has amassed considerable evidence indicating that a portion of the hypothalamus is itself sensitive to thermal stimuli. The reader will recall from Chapter IV that earlier research by Andersson also suggested this thermosensitivity by directly applying thermal stimuli to the anterior hypothalamus. In this section a closer look will be taken at the evidence pertaining to the hypothalamus as a thermal sensor. Benzinger's work can best be understood by dividing the issue into several subcategories. The topics of warm versus cold stimulation will be treated separately. In addition, the effects of temperature changes on the automatic thermoregulatory responses (e.g., sweating in the heat or increased metabolic rate in the cold) will be kept distinct from the conscious *sensations* of warmth or cold.

Warm Stimulation and Heat-dissipating Responses. To begin with, let us consider what happens to the major heat-dissipating response—sweating—under various conditions of warm stimulation. By placing thermo-sensitive devices on various places of the skin surface and via minor surgery in the inner ear, Benzinger was able to get continuous recordings of both skin and cranial temperatures. (This latter measure is an approximation of central, hypothalamic temperature.) In addition, with the use of an instrument called the *gradient calorimeter,* he was able to measure very sensitively the amount of sweating and the associated heat loss due to the evaporation of sweat. With this basic instrumentation he introduced various combinations of thermal stimuli with human subjects, such that the skin temperature and cranial temperature were driven in opposite directions. For example, consider the two following situations: (a) a subject in a very warm environment (high skin temperature) who periodically gulps down quantities of ice sherbert (reducing cranial temperature); (b) a subject in a cold environment (low skin temperature) who does strenuous exercise (producing high cranial temperature). The question asked by Benzinger was very simply: Will the production of sweat vary systematically with changes in skin temperature *or* with changes in cranial temperature? The answer, quite uniformly, turned out to be that sweat production was closely related to cranial temperature and virtually unrelated to skin

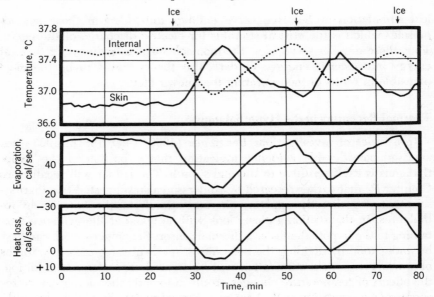

Figure 5.2 Simultaneous recordings showing relationship between internal (cranial) temperature, rates of sweating (middle chart), and heat loss from skin (bottom chart). Note that evaporation and heat-loss curves vary with internal temperature, not with skin temperature. [*Courtesy of T. H. Benzinger (1961).*]

temperature. Figure 5.2, adapted from Benzinger (1961a), shows this relationship very nicely.

Benzinger's conclusion gains considerable force when taken in conjunction with several studies which have attempted to heat directly the *anterior hypothalamus* (Magoun et al., 1938; Andersson et al., 1964). Here the sensitivity of this structure to heat was demonstrated in that heat loss responses (e.g., sweating) were produced by this thermal stimulation. Thus as the situation now stands, it appears that the anterior hypothalamus and *not* the nerves in the skin is the critical sensor for eliciting automatic, heat-dissipating responses.

As always, however, physiological processes are more complicated than they appear on the surface. In considering Benzinger's work, note two factors: (*a*) rather extreme temperatures were used and (*b*) the primary focus was on the sweating response. There is evidence that these neat findings may not always apply when considering another heat-dissipating mechanism—the dilation of peripheral blood vessels. This response, by bringing about an increased rate of blood flow from the warm interior to the cooler body surface, increases convective heat loss. Hardy (1960) suggests that, in an environment in which the temperature varies slightly around *neutral* for humans (28 to 31°C), slight changes in vasomotor tone (constriction or dilation of these peripheral blood vessels) keep heat loss and heat conservation in balance. Thus, if the environmental temperature rises somewhat, there is an immediate compensatory vasodilation which has the effect of slightly increasing body heat loss. On the other hand, if the temperature falls a bit, there is a corresponding slight vasoconstriction, thus reducing convective heat loss. A study by Forster et al., (1952) demonstrated that these vasomotor effects occurring in a thermally neutral environment appear to be controlled by thermal receptors in the skin and are *not* related in any consistent way to hypothalamic temperature.

In summary, then, the direction of evidence seems to be that, under relatively strong heat stimulation, the anterior hypothalamus serves as the critical sensor. Within a rather narrow neutral zone of environmental temperatures, however, in which heat balance is maintained largely through minimal vasomotor effects, sensors in the skin appear to be critical.

Warm Stimulation and the Sensation of Warmth. Here, again, the central question has been: What is the critical sensor for the conscious sensation of warmth, the hypothalamus or sensors in the skin? The problem facing the experimenter is twofold: (*a*) under most conditions, the skin temperature and cranial temperature covary, although the cranial temperature characteristically lags behind skin temperature as external thermal conditions change; (*b*) the experimenter usually has to rely on the verbal report of a subject to describe subtle changes in conscious experience.

Benzinger (1963) attempted to cope with these problems by having his human subject immersed up to his neck in a warm, constant-temperature bath (45°C) so that skin temperature remained at this same high temperature. Cranial temperature, however, only gradually increases under these conditions. The subject was also provided with clearly separated and well-defined verbal categories with which to communicate his thermal sensations. It was found that verbal descriptions which indicated increasing sensations of heat were given as cranial temperature increased, even though the subject's skin temperature remained constant. This again suggests that the cranial temperature (anterior hypothalamus) may be the relevant sensory organ for the conscious sensation of warmth.

This, of course, does not deny the importance of warm sensors in the skin. Reference to the exquisite sensitivity of the skin to local heating, mentioned several pages earlier, or the very immediate subjective experience of heat on touching a warm object attests to this. Benzinger, however, has provided strong evidence that conscious sensation of environmental (ambient) temperatures above normal is primarily mediated by the hypothalamus itself.

Cold Stimulation and Heat-maintaining Responses. When we consider the sensors related to automatic, thermoregulatory responses to cold stimulation, a different picture emerges. Here Benzinger et al. (1961) have demonstrated that sensors in the skin play a critical role in eliciting metabolic heat-producing responses. By applying *transient* cold stimuli via a water bath, Benzinger was able to alter skin temperature without producing measurable changes in internal cranial temperature. In response to this type of stimulation, the metabolic rate (heat production) in a human subject could be increased by three to four times its basal level, thus indicating that sensors in the skin are of major importance in eliciting the metabolic response to cold.

It should be mentioned, however, that internal, cranial temperature does play a role in the aforementioned processes. At the simplest level, Benzinger et al. (1961) have shown that the higher the cranial temperature, the less the magnitude of the metabolic heat-producing responses—up to the level where the cranial temperature is at the set point of the organism (thermal neutrality), at which point the automatic heat production ceases. Thus it appears that, although the cold receptors in the skin serve a major function in thermoregulatory heat production, hypothalamic temperature at least plays a modulating role in this process.

The importance of the cold receptors in the skin is enhanced by the findings of Hensel and Boman (1960). Using a human subject, these investigators found that the cold-receptor neurons of the skin begin to fire at an increasing rate as the skin temperature decreases. The rate of firing reaches a peak when the skin temperature has decreased to 20°C. Benzinger (1961c) finds that the maximum rate of metabolic heat production also takes place at 20°C.

Cold Stimulation and the Sensation of Cold. By using the same immersion technique described in the preceding section, Benzinger (1963) also studied the origins of conscious sensations of cold. Here, again, the conscious experience of cold (verbal report) varied systematically with changes in skin temperature. Altered levels of cranial temperature had absolutely no effect on the subject's verbal report. This latter point is in contrast to the effects on automatic heat-producing responses, where cranial temperature at least played a modulating role. It is of interest to note that the maximum sensation of cold appeared to occur at skin temperatures of about 20°C, the same point at which Hensel and Boman found peak firing of cold-receptor neurons of the skin.

Summary of Thermal Sensory System

It is hoped that the reader can now appreciate the complexity of the sensory system concerning thermal stimuli. In contrast to the analogy of the house thermostat, where the sensor is a simple thermometer mounted on a wall, the sensors in the human being are multiple and, as yet, incompletely understood. However, several salient facts stand out: (a) with respect to warm stimulation, the anterior hypothalamus seems to be the most important sensor, both for eliciting automatic heat-dissipating responses and for the conscious sensation of environmental temperature; (b) with cold stimulation, receptors in the skin play a critical role in the development of automatic heat-producing responses, although hypothalamic temperature (anterior hypothalamus, as we shall see later) also serves a modulating function; (c) the sensation of cold seems to be solely a function of receptors in the skin.

EFFECTOR-SYSTEMS

As in the earlier discussion, this section will treat the thermoregulatory responses to warm and cold stimulation separately. Space does not permit a thorough discussion of all the physiological events taking place; hence only the major systems will be reviewed.

Regulatory Responses to Heat

Three major response systems come into play when the environmental temperature is raised above thermal neutrality: (a) vasomotor (change in the status of the peripheral blood vessels), (b) sudomotor (sweating); and (c) metabolic changes (including hormonal effects). Each system has the net effect of reducing body heat, thus operating in the direction of preventing the body from overheating.

Vasomotor Changes. The transportation of heat by the convective action of warmer blood from the interior flowing to the cooler surface vessels is one of the important thermoregulatory functions of the vascular system. With the commencement of a barely noticeable increase in environmental temperature, there is an increase in heart rate that occurs within 8 seconds and a dilation of the peripheral blood vessels in 10 to 15 seconds. The over-all effect of this response of the vascular system is to increase the rate of blood flow to the surface tissues, thereby also increasing the rate of heat loss from the body.

When the environmental temperature is below the zone of neutrality for man (28 to 31°C), the vasomotor system is near a state of full constriction. In the neutral zone itself, as described earlier, very sensitive and small changes in vasomotor tone seem to be sufficient to compensate for minor variations in environmental temperature. Above the neutral zone the amount of heat loss due to the alteration of thermal conductance of the peripheral tissues is proportional to the increase in environmental temperature. At high temperatures a sixfold increase in heat conductance has been measured with the person at rest, with as high as twentyfold occurring during exercise. Thus it is apparent that dilation of the cutaneous blood vessels plays an important role in the dissipation of body heat.

Sudomotor Changes. When the environmental temperature increases above the zone of neutrality, sweating (or panting) occurs. The evaporation of this moisture on the skin surface (or in the respiratory tract) produces a cooling effect.

If the environmental temperature is gradually increased, a resting man will manifest the beginning of the sweating response at about 33°C. There is some evidence that sex, age, acclimatization, state of health, and other variables affect this threshold. In general, however, when man is exposed to a very hot and dry environment, about a 2½–fold increase in evaporation is attained within 5 minutes, and the complete sweating response occurs in 20 minutes. At these extremes, under prolonged exposure, man can put out sweat at the rate of two gallons per day. The reader will recall, however, from the chapter on thirst, that the amount of sweat produced is dependent on the state of hydration of the subject.

We are again indebted to Benzinger (1960) for some very precise data, collected from astronauts, relating sweating rate to internal cranial (hypothalamic) temperature. Figure 5.3 demonstrates the very sharp onset of the sweating response (upper line) when the cranial temperature goes beyond the subject's set point (36.9°C in this case). Note also that there is a linear increase in evaporative heat loss as the internal temperature increases (1 calorie per second for every 0.01°C increase in cranial temperature). It is of interest to note, on the lower line of the graph, the comparable changes in heat loss due to peripheral vasodilation. The sharp break in the graph occurs at a slightly lower cranial temperature, but the same linear relationship with internal temperature is apparent. Finally, it is important to note that these data look the same whether the internal cranial temperature was raised by altering the environmental temperature, by artificially raising the cranial temperature, or through strenuous activity. Evidently this internal thermostat controls the thermoregulatory responses regardless of what initiates the temperature change.

Metabolic Changes. Until now we have discussed the effector systems concerned with the *dissipation* of body heat in warm environments. As the reader might have anticipated, the question might be asked as to whether the organism's heat *production* is not also curtailed in the in-

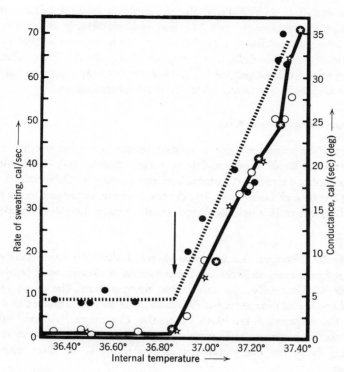

Figure 5.3 Rate of sweating and peripheral blood flow as a function of internal, cranial temperature. Above a sharply defined threshold these two "effector systems" for heat dissipation respond and rise in proportion to internal temperature. [*Courtesy of T. H. Benzinger (1960).*]

terest of thermoregulation. That is, is there a reduction in metabolic rate when exposed to high temperatures. As will be seen, the answer here is not clear cut, nor has the problem been studied extensively.

An overview of the evidence indicates that exposure to hot environments results in a lowering of body-heat production. This can be attributed most likely to reduced physical activity and a slight lowering of the basal metabolism rate. It appears that both the hypothalamus and hormonal changes (pituitary-adrenal and the pituitary-thyroid systems) are involved in this adjustment. Thus, for example, with exposure to moderate heat, there is a reduction of steroid output in the urine, indicating a lowering of activity in the pituitary-adrenal system. This hormonal system, it will be recalled, has a generally activating effect on bodily processes (MacFarlane and Robinson, 1957).

Individual differences in metabolic response to heat account for the less clear-cut data in this area. For example, a human subject in a hot environment may become irritable and restless, which, of course, would tend to increase metabolic rate. Similarly, with organisms that pant, the sheer activity of this behavior increases body heat. Thus, although a thermoregulatory lowering of body-heat production seems to take place, there are factors in operation which counteract this effect.

Regulatory Responses to Cold

In a cold environment, the responses made by organisms to maintain body heat can be divided roughly into two classes: (a) those which are heat producing (increased metabolism rate) and (b) those which tend to prevent the loss of body heat. In addition, where appropriate, in this section a distinction is made between short- versus long-term exposure to cold.

Metabolic Changes. An increase in metabolic rate can usually be expected in humans upon prolonged exposure to environmental temperatures below 28°C. Generally, the colder the temperature, the more rapid the onset of the metabolic increase. With as little as two minutes of exposure to 3°C, the response is initiated. Naturally, the magnitude and latency of the metabolic response will vary according to such factors as insulation (clothing, body fat, etc.), posture of the subject, air flow, and related variables.

A variety of responses typically occur to raise metabolic heat production in the cold. Some are automatic regulatory processes, such as shivering, tensing of muscles, increased oxygen consumption in the muscles and viscera, and various hormonal effects involving the pituitary, thyroid, and adrenal glands. Others appear to be at least partially voluntary, including such behaviors as exercising and increasing food intake. Through these various means metabolic rate may generally be increased by 50 to 100%.

Of the several responses involving the musculature, shivering in humans is the most effective. The tensing of muscles contributes minimally to the increased heat production, and exercise, although generating considerable heat, also brings about correspondingly high convective heat loss due to the flow of blood to the periphery (Hart, 1952). It has been estimated (Horvath et al., 1956) that of the various metabolic responses shivering alone can account for about 11% of the over-all body-heat production in a cold environment.

The hormonal changes which occur in the cold have aroused interest, particularly the pituitary-adrenal and the pituitary-thyroid systems. By way of review, the reader is reminded that both the adrenals and the thyroid can be activated by hormones put out by the anterior pituitary. This portion of the "master gland" appears to be, in turn, under indirect influence (via the posterior pituitary) of portions of the hypothalamus, thus emphasizing again the important coordinating role of this part of the brain.

Upon exposure to cold, thyroid activity increases immediately and remains elevated throughout prolonged cold stimulation (Cottle and Carlson, 1955). This response only occurs when the hypothalamus, pituitary, and, of course, the thyroid are intact, emphasizing the ultimate control by the hypothalamus itself. Some investigators have asserted (Ring, 1939) that this thyroid response accounts for the major part of the metabolic increase in organisms; however, there seem to be important species differences here.

In a similar fashion, steroid, adrenaline, and noradrenaline output from the adrenal cortex and adrenal medulla increases soon after exposure to cold. These responses have been observed in both human and animal subjects via blood and urine analyses. There are clear variations in output with changing seasons, indicating that this is more than an immediate response to transient cold exposure. The importance of these hormones is highlighted by the fact that experimental animals whose adrenals have been removed cannot maintain body heat and rarely survive prolonged cold exposure (Iampietro et al., 1956). Figure 5.4, adapted from Hardy (1960), represents a summary of the hormonal response to cold.

To complete this review of the metabolic response to cold, mention should be made of changes in food intake upon prolonged exposure. Several dietary surveys of servicemen in arctic climates reveal that caloric intake generally increases, but the magnitude of the increase varies with such factors as individual food preferences, amount of work performed, and adequacy of clothing. For example, servicemen at rest in a temperate climate take in about 2,670 calories per day. This increases to about 4,500 calories per day while working in an arctic climate.

As can be seen, then, the factors involved in the metabolic response to cold are multiple. The heat production required to maintain thermal balance is naturally a function of the amount of heat lost, thus making clothing and other insulation important considerations. As a cross-species generalization, it appears that the smaller the animal, the greater dependence on metabolic regulatory responses. Larger animals, usually having more fur or surface fat, tend to rely less on the hormonal and other heat-producing mechanisms. Man, of course, with all his technological skills to cope with changing thermal environments, probably relies on these mechanisms the least under ordinary circumstances.

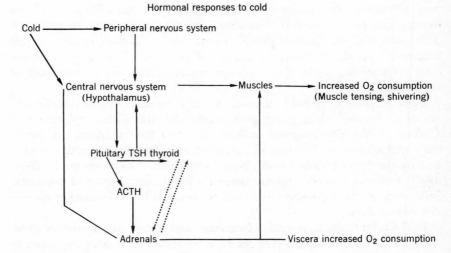

Figure 5.4 The interrelationships between central, hormonal, muscular and visceral events in response to cold. [*Courtesy of Hardy (1960).*]

Heat-conserving Responses. Brief mention should be made of the several heat-conserving responses which occur in thermal deficit. Peripheral vasoconstriction has already been reviewed as an important means of reducing convective heat exchange from the interior. Along the same line, curling up reduces the amount of body surface exposed and, thus, lowers the amount of heat lost via radiation from the body.

At a different level, long-range adaptive changes such as the development of thick fur or fatty tissue in animals should be mentioned. It has been found, for example, that for thermal insulation fat is about twice as effective as muscle tissue and about three times as effective as skin. With respect to insulation in man, the whole topic of clothing is important but cannot be treated here. The reader is referred to Burton and Edholm (1955) for a review of this subject.

CONTROLLER SYSTEMS

In this final section we come to a discussion of the centers in the brain which coordinate the sensory thermal information and the regulatory effector systems. As with most neurological research, four experimental methods have been used: (a) producing lesions; (b) electrical stimulation; (c) thermal stimulation; and (d) electrical recording from various areas of the brain. By utilizing these techniques, researchers have identified two major centers concerned with thermoregulation—the anterior and the posterior hypothalamus. Although other areas outside the hypo-thalamus have been implicated, these two centers seem to carry the major burden of the work.

Posterior Hypothalamus

This area of the hypothalamus, also known as the *heat-maintenance center*, plays a central role in coordinating responses to cold stimulation. It was first delineated shortly after the turn of the century when experi-menters systematically produced crude lesions in various parts of the hypothalami of experimental animals until they had "mapped" the region in which shivering was abolished. More recently, a series of electro-physiological studies by Birzis and Hemingway (1956, 1957) have pro-duced shivering in dogs by electrically stimulating the posterior hypo-thalamus. In addition, these same investigators were able to record al-tered electrical activity in this region in dogs who were shivering as a natural response to a cold environment. Evidence here also indicates that neural fibers emanating from this region are, via the lateral white columns of the spinal cord and probably the pyramidal tracts, the efferents sub-serving shivering.

As might be expected, the posterior hypothalamus plays a more general role than just that of controlling shivering. In a series of lesion experiments Keller and his group (Keller, 1950; Murgatroyd et al., 1958) have demon-strated that this "center" is involved in the general metabolic response to cold. With bilateral lesions the animal is unable to maintain body heat as a result of up to a fortyfold decrease in the usual metabolic response to cold.

Of particular importance is the finding that this heat-maintenance center is indifferent to thermal stimuli. Freeman and Davis (1959) demon-strated this by placing a diathermy electrode within this area and finding no measurable response to change in electrode temperature. This finding supports Benzinger's contention, reported earlier in this chapter, that the sensors for cold are in the skin, with the hypothalamic area subserving cold functioning merely as a synaptic relay station. Freeman and Davis (1959) and Benzinger (1961c), among others, have found, however, that in a cold environment the usual metabolic response is dramatically in-hibited when the *anterior* hypothalamus is warmed. This finding focuses attention on what appears to be the more important hypothalamic thermal area.

Anterior Hypothalamus

This portion of the hypothalamus has been traditionally labeled *heat-loss center* because it had been found to be an area controlling regulatory responses in warm environments. Its role in activating the sweating and vasodilation responses has been amply demonstrated in several lesion and electrical-stimulation studies (Hemingway et al., 1940). The current view, however, suggests that it is involved in the regulation of both heat-loss and heat-maintenance responses. This dual function has been observed best in studies involving the direct heating or cooling of the anterior hypothalamus.

The application of thermal stimuli via permanently implanted thermodes or diathermy electrodes to the anterior hypothalamus has been carried out in several laboratories (Magoun et al., 1938; Andersson et al., 1964). Considering the technical problems of electrode placement and possible uncontrolled tissue destruction, some surprisingly consistent results have been obtained. Warming of this area produced the full array of thermoregulatory heat-loss responses, whereas cooling produced an equal complement of the usual heat-maintenance responses. (The additional effects on drinking and eating behavior have already been covered in Chapter III.)

The control by this center over such heat-loss responses as sweating and vasodilation appears to be rather direct by way of the autonomic nervous system. On the other hand, the circuitry involved in its effects on the metabolic response to cold is at present not completely defined. Hemingway (1957) has found an efferent connection from the anterior to the posterior hypothalamus. This was demonstrated by his being able to record evoked electric potentials in these efferent fibers during electrical stimulation of the anterior area. In addition, the control of pituitary activity by portions of the hypothalamus has already been reviewed in Chapter IV. Thus there appears to be a good likelihood that the anterior hypothalamus—through its connections with both the traditional heat-maintenance center (posterior hypothalamus) and the pituitary—also plays an important role in coordinating the metabolic (and hormonal) response to cold.

THE THERMOSTATIC REGULATION OF BODY TEMPERATURE

By way of summary, let us review the analogy made to the ordinary house thermostat as it applies to physiological temperature regulation. Sensors in the skin (probably free nerve endings imbedded in the cutaneous vascular system) detect thermal changes in the cold direction, and the increased activity in these peripheral "cold" fibers is transmitted to the posterior hypothalamus and probably to the anterior hypothalamus also. There is also an apparent transmission to the cortex as well subserving the conscious sensation of cold. The posterior hypothalamus, as one part of the controller system, has been demonstrated to subserve the metabolic response to cold (shivering, increased oxygen consumption), thus in a sense "turning on the furnace." The anterior area evidently plays a co-ordinating role in this process also in that (*a*) the magnitude of the metabolic response to cold is dependent on the temperature of the anterior area and (*b*) portions of the anterior area probably interact in triggering the hormonal response to cold.

On the warm side, the anterior hypothalamus seems to act as both a sensor and controller. Warming this area elicits the effector systems of sweating and vasodilation, thus, in effect, turning on the "cooling system." Also, anterior hypothalamic control of pituitary activity seems to alter hormonal activity in the direction of lowering body heat.

Finally, the whole operation seems to be regulated by a hypothetical set-point temperature, which is probably defined in reality by a rather narrow range of temperature in the cells of the anterior hypothalamus. Deviations on either side of this set-point put into operation the complex sets of responses which tend to drive the body temperature back to the set-point.

VI

Sexual and Parental Behavior

We now arrive at a topic in which it is virtually impossible to specify the exact nature of the physiological controls on behavior. The reasons for this are varied but, in general, are due to (a) the pronounced species differences that have been found; (b) the important role played by past experience in the sexual behavior of some species; and (c) the interplay of environmental and physiological factors in determining the behavior.

An additional problem is the fact that most of the research has been done on laboratory rodents. Far less investigation has involved primates and, even less, humans. Thus cross-species generalizations are difficult, and extrapolation to humans must be tentative. With this in mind, the chapter reviews the data gathered on mammals and an attempt is made to summarize evolutionary trends where possible. Three major classes of variables are included: hormonal, neural, and experiential. Since each of these operate differently for males and females, a distinction between the sexes is maintained throughout most of the chapter.

Before proceeding, let us review a somewhat philosophical point. Taking an overview of the material in the three preceding chapters on food-, water-, and temperature-related behaviors, we can see an over-all purpose of the physiological processes involved. That is, a set of signals and effector systems were coordinated and set in motion which brought the organism back to some state of equilibrium or condition of well-being. Hence these areas, in essence, can be called *homeostatic* in nature. This does not seem to be the case with sexual behavior. Here we encounter little evidence to suggest that there is physiological deficit which accumulates or a buildup of tissue needs which is then returned to some equilibrium point as a result of sexual behavior. If there is an over-all wisdom in the physiology of sexual behavior, it seems to be of another sort: the organization and sequencing of bodily processes so that they promote conception, successful pregnancy, parturition (delivering the young), and adequate parental behaviors.

In addition it is important to point out another essential difference between sexual behaviors and those covered in the earlier chapters. Whereas food-, water-, and temperature-related behaviors appeared to be elicited by internal stimuli associated with states of disequilibrium, the role of physiological processes in sexual responses has a different emphasis. Here hormonal and neural events seem to prime the organism or produce a readiness to respond, but, to a large extent, it is external stimuli which elicit the reproductive behaviors. The primary purpose of this chapter is to review the physiological processes underlying reproductive behaviors. Nevertheless, brief mention should be made of at least the classes of external stimuli which appear to be important.

Environmental influences on sexual behaviors can be analyzed at several levels (Beach, 1951), ranging all the way from the specific sensory stimuli produced by a potential mate to such general factors as the effects of seasonal variations in temperature and illumination. It had been found, for example, as early as 1907 (Kellogg) that the males of certain species of moth depend on olfactory cues emanating from scent glands in the female for the elicitation of copulatory behaviors. Similarly, for many species of fish, visual stimuli trigger sexual responses. As we proceed up the phylogenetic scale, it appears that multiple and more complex sensory cues orient and guide behavior with respect to the mate. In primates, visual and auditory cues elicit early excitation and approach to the partner, and tactile stimulation becomes primary once physical contact is established. The reader is referred to Hinde (1966) for a thorough review of these issues.

At a more general level, situational stimuli also play an influential role in mating behaviors in that many species only reproduce in certain environs or after they (males) have established territoriality. In addition, general social factors, evidently related to roles of dominance and submission in a colony, have an effect on courtship and mating behaviors. Less dominant males frequently will not display these behaviors toward a receptive female if a more dominant male is in the vicinity (Lorenz, 1966). At the most general level, it has been known for a number of decades that such factors as temperature and illumination variables influence sexual arousal and behaviors, both in accounting for seasonal variations in some species and daily fluctuations. Some of these effects apparently are caused by altered hormonal processes, whereas still others are related to thermally induced gonadal changes (Beach, 1948).

We shall return to these issues in a somewhat different context toward the end of this chapter when experiential factors are discussed. For the moment, however, we focus our attention on the hormonal and neural factors in sexual motivation.

HORMONAL FACTORS

The effects of hormones are of most immediate importance in understanding reproductive behavior. For most of the lower mammals they are central in producing a readiness to respond with a complex sequence of mating behaviors, whereas for higher forms they seem to play an important, though supportive, role. In this discussion, the two most important sets of hormones are reviewed: (*a*) the gonadal hormones secreted by the reproductive organs themselves and (*b*) the gonadotrophic hormones secreted by the anterior pituitary gland, which, in turn, control the output of gonadal hormones. As we shall see later, the pituitary gonadotrophins are, in turn, regulated by certain nuclei of the hypothalamus, thus again emphasizing the ultimate control of this behavior by the central nervous system.

Males

Two significant processes occur in the Leydig cells of the male gonads (testis): the production of sperm cells necessary for fertilization of the female ovum and the manufacture and secretion of a class of male sex hormones—the androgens—of which testosterone and androsterone are most active. (Actually a small amount of the female hormone estrogen is also produced.) Androgens have the dual effects of promoting the growth of secondary sex characteristics at puberty (e.g., distribution of body hair, growth of beard, voice changes, growth of genitals) and the regulation of sexual behavior. In this section, the evidence pertaining to these effects is reviewed.

Androgens. As with the procedures used in studying the central nervous system, one way to evaluate the importance of a particular structure in governing behavior is to remove it surgically. Hence considerable research has been carried out on laboratory animals after they had their testes removed (castration). This procedure, of course, also stops the production of the androgens. When castration takes place before puberty in male rats, they never develop sexual behaviors. When the operation is performed on sexually experienced adult rats, there is a sharp loss in the organism's ability to show sexual excitement and a corresponding marked decline in copulatory behavior (Beach, 1958). It should be emphasized here that the surgery in no way interferes with the mechanics of carrying out mating behaviors. Rather, the rat just appears to become unmotivated.

The picture changes somewhat when male dogs or cats are used as subjects. Sexually experienced males of these species usually show a loss of responsiveness following castration, which takes about two months to manifest itself fully. However, there is a significant minority of these animals which shows only a small loss of responsiveness or copulatory behavior (Schwartz and Beach, 1954). Furthermore, with primates as subjects, wide variations in postcastration behavior can be observed. Many experienced males show no loss of sexual behavior. Even with castration before puberty, some sexual behavior develops, although this tends to be lethargic and mechanical (Clark, 1945).

Hence there are cross-species differences in response to castration. The lower the organism in the mammalian scale, the more directly dependent is sexual behavior on the hormonal output of the testes. At the other end of the continuum this trend is exemplified in human males as well, where the dependence on the androgens is the least of all. These species differences are encountered in most of the research literature on sex.

To be scientifically precise, we would have to admit that the studies described in the foregoing do not prove that the androgens are the critical agents affecting male sexual responsiveness, even with the rat subjects. It is possible that some effect of castration other than the loss of gonadal hormones is the relevant factor. This problem of scientific inference has been very neatly clarified by studies in which synthetic androgens have been administered to castrates. This sort of "replacement therapy" has a very marked and observable effect on the unresponsive male rat. There is a return of normal sexual responsiveness; furthermore, the increase in the amount of copulatory behavior is directly related to the amount of androgens administered (Beach and Fowler, 1959). Thus there is evidence from this second source pointing to the androgens as an important factor in male sexuality.

As in the castration studies, the higher we go up the phylogenetic scale, the less predictable are the effects of replacement therapy. In primates and, even more so, in human males, there are marked individual differences in response to androgen administration. Beach (1958), who is one of the leading investigators in this area, points out that in these higher forms the effects of learning and past experience play the major role; hence hormonal effects are probably overshadowed by these more potent variables.

Gonadotrophic Hormone. Mention was made in the introductory section that androgen production was regulated by another hormone which is secreted by the anterior pituitary gland. Surgical removal of the pituitary should thus have the same debilitating effect as castration. This is indeed the case. Extirpation of this gland leads to a dramatic loss of sexual behavior and a general regression of the sexual apparatus. Again, replacement therapy by either androgens or gonadotrophic hormone restores the apparatus and the behavior. These findings are again subject to the same cross-species trends found earlier. That is, with the lower mammalian forms the loss and subsequent restoration are complete and clear cut; with the higher forms the sexual loss due to extirpation is variable, as is the restoration with replacement therapy (Goy, 1964). It should be kept in mind also that removal of the anterior pituitary has more widespread effects which make interpretation of the data difficult. The reader will recall that this portion of the pituitary also secretes trophic hormones which influence the thyroid and adrenal cortex particularly, thus producing general metabolic change as well.

Females

Hormonal factors in the female mammalian reproductive system are considerably more complex than those in males. This is owing to (a) the cyclical nature of the system; (b) the broader array of gonadal and pituitary hormones involved; and (c) the different processes which take place depending on whether or not pregnancy occurs. In primates the relevant cycle for the present discussion is called the *menstrual cycle,* which is delineated by the interval between periods of uterine discharge. In subprimates it is called *the estrous cycle*—which varies markedly in time across species—defined by the interval between periods of sexual receptivity or "heat." Perhaps the best place to begin would be a description of the female reproductive cycle along with its various hormones. As will be seen, sexual behavior, particularly in the lower mammals, is regulated very closely by events taking place in this cycle.

Ovarian Cycle. The female gonads—the ovaries—serve a dual function: the production of egg cells (ova) and the secretion of hormones. Events within the ovary follow a definite sequence, which in humans takes about 28 days, following which a new cycle begins. At the beginning of the cycle, many immature ova within the ovary are each surrounded by a single layer of tissue called *follicular cells.* These structures are called *primary follicles.* Under the influence of an anterior pituitary trophic hormone, appropriately called the *follicle-stimulating hormone* (FSH), generally only one ovum and its surrounding cells begin to grow. This growth process continues for the first half of the cycle. These maturing follicular cells constitute the tissue which secretes the ovarian hormone *estrogen,* so that over this growth period there is also a progressive rise in estrogen level.

Throughout this initial half of the cycle there is another anterior pituitary gonadotrophin called *luteinizing hormone* (LH) which is being secreted at low levels. FSH and LH act together to control the amount of estrogen produced by the maturing follicle. Toward the end of the first half of the cycle, there is a sudden increase in the amount of LH secreted by the pituitary and, under the influence of this elevated level, the ovum breaks through the wall of the follicle and the ovary. This phenomenon, known as *ovulation,* is the period during the cycle when the female is fertile, i.e., the ovum is capable of being fertilized by male spermatozoa. It is of interest to note that, under the influence of the high level of estrogen produced just prior to ovulation, the female's sexual receptivity is at a peak. Thus in the lower mammals at least, copulation generally occurs at a point in the cycle when conception is most likely to take place.

Following ovulation, the secretions of FSH and LH decline rapidly. The character of the ruptured follicle also changes in that a new set of cells becomes predominant. These cells are called *luteal cells* and the whole structure is now termed the *corpus luteum.* This body secretes low levels of estrogen and another ovarian hormone, *progesterone.* These hormonal secretions by the corpus luteum are, in turn, controlled by a third pituitary gonadotrophic hormone which has not yet been completely identified, but is probably the substance *prolactin.* Progesterone is functionally important in that it prepares the female's body for gestation, i.e., the nurturance of the fertilized ovum. Among other effects of progesterone, the most important at this stage is the change brought about in the tissues of the uterus. These cells now become highly vascularized and irregular, thus promoting the attachment of the fertilized ovum to the wall of the uterus where, of course, it will reside as a maturing organism until birth. Under these conditions the corpus luteum remains intact, secreting progestrone until specialized structures in the uterus itself can develop to take over the functions of maintaining the growing embryo.

If fertilization does not take place, the corpus luteum gradually atrophies over the second half of the cycle, with a concomitant drop in its hormonal output. At the end of this phase then, the specialized tissue in the uterus and its blood content are reabsorbed or discharged, bringing to an end the hormonal cycle. Figure 6.1 presents a schematic of the ovarian and hormonal changes which occur during these processes.

By way of summary, several biologically significant aspects of the female cycle should be reemphasized. Of primary interest is the fact that, during the first half of the cycle, the pituitary and ovarian hormones are sequenced in such a way that behaviorally the female has a period of high sexual receptivity just prior to ovulation—a very necessary phasing of physiological and behavioral events to bring about conception and ulti-

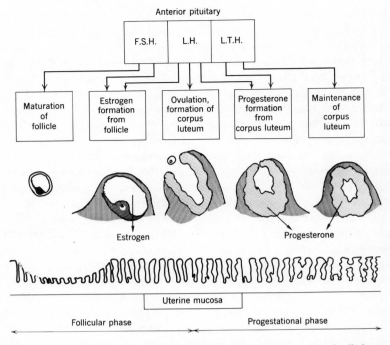

Anterior pituitary

Figure 6.1 Summary of the relationship between pituitary "trophic" hormones, ovarian events, and uterine changes. (From T.R. Harrison, et al., *Principles of Internal Medicine*, 3rd ed. McGraw-Hill Book Company, 1958.)

mately the propagation of the species. Secondly, hormonal changes during the latter half of the cycle are organized in such a way as to favor the implantation and nurturance of a fertilized ovum in the uterine tissues—again an equally significant event for the carrying of offspring.

Regulation of Hormones. The rather complex rise and fall in the levels of the various female hormones just described may have prompted the reader to wonder about the factors governing their secretion. The answers here are not completely available, but at least one aspect of the process has been investigated. There is evidence (Lloyd and Leathem, 1964) that the ovarian hormones, estrogen and progesterone, which are controlled by the pituitary hormones, have feedback effects on the hypothalamus, which, in turn, governs the pituitary gonadotrophins. For example, when the rising estrogen production during the first half of the cycle reaches a critical level in the blood stream, it seems to have a return effect on the pituitary, provoking increased secretion of LH. In the same way, after ovulation, the high levels of estrogen and progesterone in the blood stream have an inhibitory effect on the pituitary's secretion of FSH and LH, and these two rapidly decline. Finally, by the end of the cycle, when estrogen and progesterone levels are low, this relative deficiency releases the pituitary from inhibition and the secretion of FSH begins to rise. Thus another cycle is initiated.

These hormonal feedback effects are obviously an incomplete description of the controls on the system. As mentioned earlier, the hypothalamus is intimately involved in pituitary functions and the feedback mechanisms described in the foregoing. These effects will be elaborated later in the section on neural factors. Suffice it to say for now that a vast amount of research is still needed to detail the regulation of these hormones.

Hormones and Female Sexual Behavior

Sexual receptivity in laboratory rodents occurs only during those periods when the estrogen level is high (estrous), i.e., around the time of ovulation. At this time she will approach males, appears to be exciting to males, and, of course, will permit copulation. At other times, when estrogen levels are lower, the female rat will not permit sexual approaches and, furthermore, does not appear to be exciting to males (see Beach, 1958).

This dependence on estrogen level is most clearly demonstrated in studies where the ovaries of a sexually experienced female rat are removed (Beach, 1947). This produces a quick and permanent loss of sexual receptivity. Hormonal replacement therapy brings about a return of normal sexual behavior.

In female primates the period of receptivity is still closely related to the menstrual cycle, with sexual behavior again occurring during the time of high estrogen level. Females of this mammalian class rarely engage in sexual activity at other times in the cycle, although there have been enough exceptions to this rule to make a point of it (Beach, 1958). During these latter engagements, however, the female's performance is again mechanical and uninspired.

Ovariectomy and subsequent replacement therapy with estrogen in female primates have the expected effects. Sexual behavior is lost in the majority of animals, with a few exceptions still maintaining sporadic contacts with males. Replacement treatment generally brings about a temporary return of receptivity, again with the usual few individual differences in response. The point here is that, although the sexual behavior of the female primates is certainly influenced by nonphysiological factors such as prior experience and preferences for one male over another, the major influence still appears to be hormonal.

As might be expected, removal of the anterior pituitary, thereby abolishing the hormones which regulate ovarian events, has comparable effects on these organisms. The loss of sexual behavior is rapid and profound, but can be reestablished with hormonal replacement therapy. The same cross-species differences are found in these studies, with hormonal influences becoming progressively less important as we proceed up the mammalian scale.

NEURAL FACTORS

The two principal areas to be covered in this section are the cortex and the hypothalamus. With respect to the former it is interesting to note that a cross-species trend is apparent that parallels the trend found with hormonal factors. That is, as we proceed up the phylogenetic scale and get progressively more influence from experiential, learning factors, the cortex assumes greater importance in mediating sexual behavior. As will be seen, however, the hypothalamus still plays a central, integrating role in the behavior.

Cortex

Male rats can tolerate up to 20% removal of the cortex and still show normal sexual behavior. With between 20 to 60% removal of the cortex there are variable effects; but generally, the greater the lesion, the more pronounced are the adverse effects (Beach, 1940). With males of higher forms, the cat, for example, the adverse effects of comparable damage to parts of the cortex are somewhat more severe (Beach et al., 1955). As might be expected, primate and human males are even more severely debilitated with loss of cortical tissue. A rather common-sense generalization seems to handle these trends in the data. In the higher forms, three important aspects of behavior are mediated by the cortex: (a) the organization of complex motor behaviors; (b) the reception and interpretation of sensory information; and (c) the storage and utilization of learned experiences. Thus, as can be seen, damage to the cortex in these higher forms can readily interfere with (a) the complex pursuit and mounting behaviors of males; (b) maintaining sustained arousal which depends on visual, olfactory, and other sensory cues; and (c) the organization of learned sequences of courtship and copulatory behaviors (Beach, 1958).

With females the dependence on the cortex is considerably less. In mammals up to the level of the dog, complete decortication does not substantially reduce mating behavior. This again parallels the greater control exerted by hormones in females that was noted in the previous section and the relatively passive postural and muscular adjustments required for mating. Although no clear-cut experimental evidence is available on primate or human females, the trend again seems to be toward increasing reliance on the cortex in carrying out sexual behavior (Beach, 1958).

Hypothalamus

Adequate treatment of the hypothalamus and sexual behavior necessitates a review of its interaction with the pituitary. It will be recalled that the gonadotrophic hormones secreted by the anterior pituitary directly control the production of both the male and female sex hormones, which, in turn, are instrumental in eliciting sexual motivation. We now look at the connections between the hypothalamus and the pituitary to get some perspective on how this central-nervous-system structure influences the hormonal systems.

Excitatory Effects. Figure A.3 shows the position and connections between the two lobes of the pituitary and various nuclei of the hypothalamus. Note that fibers from regions of the hypothalamus funnel into the posterior lobe of the gland. Notice also that there are no direct neural connections between the hypothalamus and the anterior lobe, i.e., that part of the pituitary which secretes the gonadotrophins. Anatomical and biochemical studies, however, have revealed that the neurosecretions from areas of the hypothalamus into the median eminence are transported over a portal system into the anterior pituitary. Thus hypothalamic control of the anterior pituitary seems to be a two-stage process: neural processes in the hypothalamus initiate the secretion of biochemical substances and these "releasing factors" are transmitted over a vascular network to the anterior pituitary where they trigger gonadotrophic hormones (Everett, 1964).

Evidence for this hypothalamic control of the gonadotrophins is plentiful. In one type of study the anterior pituitary is surgically removed and transplanted in a new location in the body (e.g., the kidney) where it becomes functionally capable of producing hormones. However, in the absence of its connections with the hypothalamus, it does *not* secrete gonadotrophins. If, however, it is transplanted to its usual position adjacent to the hypothalamus in another animal whose pituitary has also been removed, the vascular connections regenerate and the gonadotrophic secretions are reinstituted (Harris, 1955a).

Another line of evidence is represented by studies in which specific lesions are made in the hypothalamus. An important question that has arisen in connection with lesioning studies is whether sexual behavior is affected because (a) the hypothalamic areas controlling gonadotrophic hormone secretions have been damaged or (b) some more basic neural area which normally elicits sexual behavior has been disrupted. Species differences and incomplete data prevent a simple generalization here, but at least a partial picture is emerging with respect to this issue. Sawyer (1960), for example, has found in cats that hypothalamic lesions in the region of the mammillary nuclei (an area posterior to the ventromedial nucleus) abolished sexual behavior, but this effect could be reversed by estrogen-replacement therapy. This suggested that the sexual deficits produced by these lesions were attributable to a disruption of gonado-trophic hormone mechanisms. Sawyer found a similar effect in rabbits when the lesions were placed slightly more anterior, in the region of the ventromedial nucleus. These and similar results (Everett, 1964) suggest that the basal tuberal region (the approximate area of the ventromedial nucleus in Figure A.3) controls gonadotrophic secretions in the species thus far studied. This conclusion also draws support from several studies in which sites within the tuberal region were electrically stimulated, resulting in changes in pituitary gonadotrophic secretions (Harris, 1955*b*).

When lesions are made in the anterior hypothalamus, a different pattern of results is obtained. Brookhart et al. (1941) found that sexual behavior in guinea pigs was abolished with anterior lesions and that it could not be reinstated with hormonal replacement therapy. In addition, they found no regression in the sexual apparatus following these lesions, indicating that the hormonal mechanisms had most likely not been altered. Comparable results have been obtained by other investigators (Sawyer and Robinson, 1956), suggesting that areas in the anterior hypothalamus (particularly the supraoptic and paraventricular nuclei) are essential in the elicitation of sexual behavior, and that these effects are not mediated by alterations in gonadotrophic or gonadal hormone mechanisms.

The implication that certain anterior hypothalamic sites are important in the evocation of organized sexual responses has received support from several studies in which these areas have been chemically stimulated via gonadal hormones. Fisher (1956) found that male rats exhibited sexual responses after injections of testosterone into certain areas of the preoptic nucleus. Other sites of stimulation in this region elicited maternal behaviors. More recently, Michael (1962) has demonstrated that certain cells in the anterior hypothalamus of female cats are sensitive to estrogen. When stimulated by the introduction of estrogen directly on the cells, the cats displayed exaggerated and intense sexual responses.

We begin to see then the possibility of some interesting feedback mechanisms involving hormonal-neural integration of sexual motivation. Starting with the tuberal region of the hypothalamus, there is evidently considerable control of gonadotrophic hormone secretions from the pituitary. These, in turn, affect the secretion of gonadal hormones, which via vascular transport presumably have a return effect on certain bio-chemically sensitive cells in the anterior hypothalamus. These latter sites seem to have a direct effect of eliciting sexual behavior when thus stimu-lated. These feedback mechanisms probably also have a secondary effect pertaining to the regulation of gonadotrophic hormones.

Other Hormonal and Neural Factors

Areas of the limbic system have also received attention with respect to sexual behavior. Kluver and Bucy (1939) in a well-known study observed marked hypersexuality (masturbation, indiscriminate mounting) in the male monkey following temporal lobe lesions. Schreiner and Kling (1953, 1954, 1956) studied the effects of lesions of the amygdala in males in a variety of species (cats, agoutis, and lynx) and again found hypersexuality. This effect was removed by castration, but could be reinstated by hormone therapy, again suggesting another general site for hormonal-neural inter-action in sexual behavior. More recently Altman and Das (1965) have presented evidence indicating that cells in the hippocampus as well may be responsive to gonadal hormones which may affect sexual behavior via efferents to the hypothalamus.

MacLean and his coworkers (1962, 1963) have found through electrical stimulation of a variety of sites in the limbic system (amygdala and hippocampus) and hypothalamus such partial sexual behaviors as penile erection and ejaculation. Miller (1961), by stimulating portions of the hypothalamus of rats, elicited the ejaculation response, as did Herberg (1963) via stimulation in the area of the medial forebrain bundle (major fiber tracts from the limbic system to the hypothalamus). It is interesting to note that the hypothalamic area producing ejaculation in the Miller study was also found to be a "reward" area when a self-stimulation experimental technique was used; i.e., rats would work at a behavioral task, the only consequent being brief, electrical stimulation (via an im-planted electrode) to this site. This issue will be reviewed in some detail in the discussion of reinforcement in Chapter VIII. We see then from the previous discussion that, although areas of the hypothalamus appear to be central in the control of sexual responses (at least in lower mammals), portions of the limbic system are also implicated. The precise nature of these limbic influences and their relationships to other motivational sys-tems which appear to be involved in this area have yet to be worked out.

Summary of Neural Factors

It is apparent from the foregoing sections that our knowledge of the neurology of sexual behavior is incomplete. Several factors do, however, seem to be reasonably well demonstrated, particularly in the lower mammalian species.

1. Areas of the hypothalamus (probably in the tuberal region) initiate the secretion of gonadotrophic hormones from the anterior pituitary.

2. These, in turn, control the production of gonadal hormones, of which the androgens in males and estrogen in females are directly correlated with sexual excitability and behavior.

3. There is a strong likelihood that the behavioral effects of these hormones are mediated by their return effect on other, as yet not completely identified, cells in the anterior hypothalamus and, possibly, on areas of the limbic system. These cells, if stimulated hormonally, appear to be capable of eliciting sexual responses in the intact organism.

4. As we proceed up the mammalian scale, the role of the cortex in subserving the complex sensorimotor and learned aspects of copulatory behavior becomes increasingly important, particulary in males.

EXPERIENTIAL FACTORS

We arrive now at factors which are obviously crucial in governing human sexual behavior. Unfortunately, however, there are very little data which provide a clear picture of the processes involved at the human level. Again, some research has been carried out with lower forms, and we must be content simply to project trends in the data up to humans.

Learning in Males

It is quite clear that the acquisition of sexual behavior in the male rat involves little learning. When raised in complete isolation until after puberty, the male shows normal mating responses when first placed with a receptive female (Beach, 1942). The same generalization holds for male cats and dogs as well. Hence mating responses in these animals appear to be built into the behavioral repertoire and simply are triggered by the appropriate hormonal and environmental conditions and the presence of a receptive female.

This does not appear to be the case with male primates, however. Observations by Nissen (1953) indicate that trial-and-error learning with an experienced female is necessary before the chimpanzee can carry out effective mating behaviors. Primates reared in isolation until after puberty do show normal sexual arousal when placed with a receptive female. They do not however, appear capable of executing appropriate sexual behaviors—usually making abnormal postural adjustments or abnormal approach movements toward the female. The work of Harlow (1962) with macaque monkeys substantiates these findings and will be discussed further at the end of this chapter.

Once more, then, the phylogenetic trend is suggested: the lower the organism, the less likely does learning play a role in the initial acquisition of the male's mating behavior. This is not to say, however, that the male rat's sexual behavior is unmodifiable by experiential factors. There have been numerous studies demonstrating that mating responses are subject to learning influences, as are most other complex behaviors. For example, if a male rat is given a painful electric shock each time he attempts to copulate with a female, a marked and fairly lengthy inhibition of sexual behaviors results (Beach et al., 1956). In addition, as we go up the phylogenetic scale, such learned inhibitions become potentially more complex until, in man, we encounter the widest variety of culturally learned rules and mores governing sexual behavior.

In contrast to these inhibitory effects, learning variables can also play a role in producing sexual arousal. Using male rats, Beach and Zitrin (1945) repeatedly presented a neutral stimulus each time a rat was undergoing sexual satisfaction. After several such associations, presentation of the neutral stimulus itself was adequate to produce sexual arousal. Here, again, comparable procedures with higher organisms bring about even more complex forms of conditioned arousal. In man, of course, the most elaborate forms of this type of learning are displayed—all the way from the arousing qualities of suggestive jokes to the quiet yearning produced on seeing a memento of an old beau.

Learning in Females

Female rats, cats, and dogs, upon first coming into heat at puberty, mate readily and appropriately with an experienced male. Thus, again, learning factors seem to be insignificant in the development of mating behaviors in the females of these species. However, with the higher forms, as with male primates trial-and-error-learning is important in the acquisition of effective copulatory responses (Harlow, 1962).

In contrast to males, however, the sexual behavior of females on the lower end of the scale seems to be largely unaffected by experiential factors. Regardless of the types of learning experiences that had taken place during rearing, the postpuberal female rat mates readily when estrogen level is high, again reflecting the primary control by hormonal factors and the relative insignificance of learned (cortical) factors. Once again, however, this is not the case with females of higher forms (primates), where experience does affect such diverse behaviors as preferences for a particular male or the development of refinements of the copulatory sequence itself.

Social Variables

Human sexual behavior, although still an outgrowth of the biological processes heretofore discussed, appears to be subject to major influences by cultural and interpersonal variables. Certainly, the last 50 years have seen the gradual decline in taboos regarding the scientific study of this area, beginning with Freud's theory of psychosexual development at the turn of the century through the sociological work of Kinsey et al. (1948), and the more recent descriptions of the human sexual response by Masters and Johnson (1966). Illustrative data may suggest some of the directions taken by research concerning these social variables.

One aspect of the Kinsey et al. (1948) work was concerned with the relationship between social class and premarital intercourse in American males. Dividing their sample into three groups on the basis of educational level attained, these authors found substantial differences in premarital sexual behaviors. Of the males with less than an eighth grade education 57% had indulged in sexual intercourse by age 15, compared with only 15% in the group which had at least one year of college. By age 21, these percentages had increased to 84% for the low-education group and to 49% for the college group. However, it was also found that relative to the low-education subjects, the higher educational group manifested a higher incidence of other forms of sexual expression (masturbation, petting to climax, etc.).

Along somewhat different lines, Winch (1949) investigated the courtship behaviors of adolescents from broken and intact homes. Here it was found, via interview techniques, that both males and females who had lost one or both parents either through death or divorce showed deficits in the ability to carry out normal courtship patterns and displayed negative attitudes toward sex generally. Although the level of data is considerably different (interview versus behavioral observation), these results are consistent with those of Harlow and Harlow (1962) with primate subjects.

A number of large-scale attitude surveys (e.g., Purdue Opinion Poll, 1961) reveal the very great importance of what might be termed the *human affectional response* in determining courtship and mating behaviors. These data suggest that sexual responsiveness to another is surprisingly little affected by physical characteristics of the partner. Rather such qualities as being "affectionate," "understanding," or "trustworthy" appear to be the critical factors in the courtship patterns leading up to adolescent and young adult sexual behavior.

Although necessarily abbreviated, the foregoing section illustrates the types of data that have been collected concerning social variables on the human sexual response. Quite obviously, the behavioral norms of the social group to which one belongs help define "correct" or acceptable sexual behavior. Similarly, more immediate transmission of behavior patterns, information, and attitudes regarding sexuality and interpersonal affection occurs within the family unit, and in the American culture, at least, this type of learning seems to emphasize the importance of personal rather than physical qualities of potential mates in the regulation of courtship patterns.

PARENTAL BEHAVIOR

The behavior of the female mammal toward her offspring is still one of the mysteries of psychology. Although considerable experimental data have been obtained which point to a number of critical variables, no satisfactory integration of this information is yet available. In this concluding section, then, a brief review of the research literature is presented under the several categories of parental behavior: nest building, nursing, and affectional responses.

Nest Building

Just as human parents prepare for the birth of a child by buying a crib and assorted accessories, mammals of lower forms prepare a place in which to care for their young. This nest building in rats, for example, seems to be closely related to hormonal events during pregnancy and the estrous cycle. The pregnant rat usually shows a marked increase in nest-building activities about five days prior to parturition. This is a period when her progesterone level is high. This relationship to the pregnancy hormone is also reflected in the nonpregnant female's nesting behavior, being virtually nonexistent during the ovulation portion of the estrous cycle and being highest toward the end of the sequence when, again, progesterone level is high. The most direct line of evidence on this point, however, appears in studies in which progesterone was administered to nonpregnant rats, resulting in an increase in nest-building behavior (Koller, 1956). Thus it is relatively clear that hormonal factors play a role. It has also been observed that nest building increases as the environmental temperature drops. Along the same lines, removal of the rat's thyroid (which interferes with thermoregulation in the cold) produces a sharp increase in nest building (Richter, 1942).

These physical variables (hormones and temperature) cannot, however, completely account for nest-building behavior. Of particular interest is the observation that the presence of newborn rats is usually a stimulus for building adequate shelter. Hence, even though the progesterone level in the mother declines sharply after giving birth, she continues to construct a nesting place when her litter is present. Furthermore, it has been noted that, when infant rats are placed in the cage of a nonpregnant female, the amount of nest building increases significantly (Koller, 1956). Hence it seems that sensory-social factors also are involved in this form of parental behavior.

Nursing

In mammals the providing of nourishment to the young through nursing is, of course, an indispensable aspect of parental behavior. This process again represents an interesting interplay between hormonal and external stimuli.

The production of milk in the mammary glands is very clearly under the control of the anterior pituitary hormone, prolactin. The level of this substance rises just prior to birth and remains high until the pups are weaned. The central role played by prolactin has been demonstrated by studies in which the pituitary had been removed (with subsequent loss of milk production) followed by replacement therapy with prolactin (which restores the mammary secretion).

The process of actually making milk available to the suckling pup, however, is somewhat more complex. Although milk is secreted by the mammary gland under the influence of prolactin, it does not enter the region of the nipple until it is "let down." This "milk ejection reflex" is initiated by the mechanical stimulus of the pup's suckling behavior which, in turn, initiates the secretion of the posterior pituitary hormone, oxytocin. It is this substance, circulating through the blood stream, which produces the "letting down" of the milk. Oxytocin has the additional effect of stimulating further production of prolactin. We see here then an interplay between the mechanical stimulus of suckling and two hormones which are sequenced in such a way as to provide a long-term supply of nourishment for the young.

Affectional Behavior

Everyday observation reveals the fact of an affectional bond between mother and infant. The maternal dependency of infant mammals for food, warmth, and protection were thought to be the basis for the development of this affection. In recent years, however, Harlow et al. (1958, 1959) have focused attention on yet another aspect of filial behavior—the role of physical contact with the mother. In Harlow's experiments with infant monkeys, inanimate substitute mothers were used which varied dramatically in their design. One mother was constructed with a wood base covered with sponge rubber and terrycloth, thereby making it soft to the touch. The other surrogate mother was of the same general shape, but had a wire surface, thus providing little tactual comfort. Although several variations were used, the important condition for the present discussion was the situation where the wire mother was provided with a milk source, whereas the soft mother was not. The infants, isolated from all other social contacts, were kept in an enclosure which provided free access to each surrogate mother; in effect, the infants had to rely on these two inanimate objects for all their "mothering."

Of particular interest was the finding that the infants spent virtually all their contact time with the cloth mother, even though it was the wire mother that provided them with food. Other tests showed that the infants also relied on the cloth mother for security and protection, running to "her" with relatively great frequency when fright was experimentally induced. Harlow points out that the behaviors developed toward the cloth mother appear to be similar to the affectional ties of infant monkeys to real mothers. Moreover, it was found that this relationship persisted over time and could survive rather long separations from the cloth mother. On the basis of these findings, Harlow suggested that with respect to maternal-filial relationships, an important need system is evident, which involves physical contact and the concomitant tactual stimulation. This system, apparently independent of food-related motivation, was considered an important area of concern with respect to later social development.

A later series of studies (Harlow, 1962; Harlow and Harlow, 1962) followed up the subsequent social development of these inanimately reared monkeys. Deviant social behaviors were apparent, comparable with those observed in monkeys reared in complete isolation. These animals, in varying degrees, showed inability to carry out mating behaviors (although there was some interest displayed) and frequently exhibited defensive or aggressive behaviors when approached by peers. Lastly, of the few females that did mate and produce offspring, there were indications that maternal behaviors were deficient.

Harlow also observed the development of infant monkeys who were reared without mothers but who were permitted interactions with peers. In later social processes, these subjects appeared to be relatively normal, suggesting that the behavioral, social, and emotional learning which takes place in peer relationships during early maturational stages may be of equal, if not of greater, importance than the infant-maternal relationship (Harlow and Harlow, 1962).

VII

Response to Aversive Stimulation

The phenomenon of pain has been a notoriously difficult one to define. It is an experience which has immediacy and compelling qualities which clearly place it within the general study of motivation. Yet upon casual observation, we observe such wide individual differences in response to aversive stimulation and such varied reports on the subjective feelings aroused that the phenomenon remains an elusive one. Traditionally, two scientific approaches have been adopted in the study of pain: (a) its behavioral effects and (b) a description of the physiological processes involved. Unfortunately, these two areas of study have heretofore remained relatively independent. Only in recent years have attempts been made to provide an integrated view of the organism's reactions to noxious events. The aim of this chapter is to attempt an overview of this integrated response.

In keeping with this aim, the chapter is organized into three sections: (a) the first is a review of the behavioral responses to painful stimulation; (b) the second summarizes the physiological processes that occur during pain; and (c) a brief section on some of the relationships between these two levels of response.

VARIETIES OF AVERSIVE CONDITIONS

Noxious stimulation can have radically different effects on behavior depending on its relationship to that behavior. In one case, the application of painful stimuli will weaken ongoing responses, whereas in another situation it may strengthen behavior. In this brief opening section, several different paradigms involving aversive events are reviewed, to be followed by a more detailed section describing the effects of each paradigm on behavior.

The Punishment Paradigm. Probably the most familiar application of aversive stimulation is that which has been termed *punishment.* In its simplest form this can be described as a situation in which a particular response is followed by a noxious stimulus. In everyday experiences the most frequent example would be that of a child who does something naughty and is then spanked by the parent.

The Escape Paradigm. In this situation, the noxious stimulus is ongoing and the emission of a particular behavior terminates the stimulation. A typical laboratory arrangement for the escape procedure might involve a rat receiving continuous electric shock while in an enclosure until he either presses a bar to terminate the current or finds a way to escape the enclosure.

The Avoidance Paradigm. This situation is related to the escape procedure except that the noxious stimulus is absent and the organism's behavioral response prolongs its absence. Thus the rat in a Skinner box might be subjected to the following arrangement: The electric shock stays off for 10 seconds. If the rat presses the bar before the 10 seconds are up, the shock is delayed for another 10 seconds. Thus by responding at least once during every interval, the rat can avoid the shock.

The Conditioned Emotional-Response Paradigm. In this somewhat more complex procedure, a new element is added. A neutral stimulus regularly precedes the occurrence of a noxious stimulus. After repeated pairings, the previously neutral stimulus will acquire the ability to elicit emotional-like behaviors itself. In addition, this *conditioned* stimulus can now be utilized as an aversive stimulus in any of the aforementioned paradigms. Naturally, if the conditioned stimulus is no longer paired with a directly painful event, it will eventually lose its aversive properties. There are many common examples of this phenomenon in our everyday lives. Within the realm of parent-child relations, consider the situation of a two-year old who is just acquiring language. Quite frequently the parent will say, "No, don't do that" and then spank the child. After several such episodes, the verbal statement alone is enough to elicit fearful responses in the child. This form of conditioned emotional response is of great theoretical importance in understanding complex human emotional responses because it suggests how a wide variety of neutral stimuli can acquire aversive properties.

BEHAVIORAL RESPONSES TO AVERSIVE STIMULATION

In the following section an attempt is made to summarize the relationships among the various aversive procedures mentioned previously and their effects on behavior. It should be recognized that electric shock has been the most widely used noxious event in laboratory experiments, mainly because it can be controlled and specified with reasonable accuracy. This may be viewed as a limitation on the generality of the data emerging from these studies.

Punishment and Behavior

When noxious stimulation regularly follows a particular behavior, we ordinarily assume that this punishment weakens the behavior. Research over the last several years indicates, however, that this is not a simple relationship. The behavioral effects are dependent on several variables, the more important ones being (a) the intensity of the punishment (b) the time delay between behavior and noxious event, and (c) the subject's prior exposure to punishment.

With respect to the intensity variable, a rather regular relationship seems to have been found. As one increases the magnitude of the punishing stimulus from minimal to intense, the punished behavior becomes more and more suppressed. Several stages of this effect have been delineated:

1. With mild punishment, the noxious stimulus is merely detected by the organism but there is no measurable effect on behavior.

2. Somewhat more intense punishment leads to temporary suppression of the behavior, which recovers fully even during the latter stages of the procedure.

3. An even greater intensity results in a partial suppression of the behavior without complete recovery.

4. Punishment at high intensities is associated with complete suppression of the punished behavior, without recovery (e.g., Azrin, 1960; Karsh, 1962). Thus this intensity variable seems to affect at least two aspects of behavior—the degree to which it is inhibited during the punishment procedure and the permanancy of the suppression.

The time lapse between response and noxious stimulation (delay of punishment) also displays the expected relationship. Obviously, the longer the delay, the less the suppression of behavior (Kamin, 1959). Thus a young child who gets punished in the evening for a transgression committed that morning is not likely to show much suppression of the incorrect behavior. However, it has been demonstrated that this sort of almost random noxious stimulation has a generally suppressing effect on all behavior, particularly if the punishment is intense (Annau and Kamin, 1961).

Prior exposure to punishment produces some interesting data. It has been pointed out (Church, 1963) that, if we speculated about the effect of

Behavioral Responses to Aversive Stimulation   103

earlier punishment, two different predictions are possible. On one hand it might be reasoned that prior exposure produces a resistance to the disruptive effects of shock and, thus, current punishment should have a reduced behavioral effect. This can be termed an *adaptation* hypothesis. An alternate line of reasoning suggests that the earlier exposure would make the organism more emotional and, hence, more susceptible to the behavioral suppression effect. In actuality, the data lend support to the adaptation notion. That is, if the organism has been exposed to a graded series of electric shocks (gradually increasing the intensity), punishment has a reduced effectiveness in suppressing behavior (Miller, 1960; Azrin, 1960).

With respect to simple punishment procedures, then, the data (collected on rats) seem to be superficially clear. It has been pointed out, however (Bandura, 1962), that the effects on humans and, particularly children, may be more complex. If, for example, a parent frequently utilizes punishment as a means of discipline, the child may develop a general avoidance response to the parent and/or learn to imitate the parent and thus behave in an aggressive, punitive way in other situations. These and some other paradoxical effects of punishment will be reviewed in a later section.

Escape Behavior

Under this procedure, it is again not surprising to find that the intensity of the aversive stimulation is the major variable. This was demonstrated in a now classic experiment by Campbell and Kraeling (1953) in which rats were shocked through an electrified grid floor in one section of a straight alley. The rats could escape the shock by running down the alley to a "safe" goal box. These investigators varied the intensity of the shock (200, 300, 400 volts) and measured the running speed of the rats. The data indicated that during the early trials, when the escape response was being learned, the running speed was proportional to shock intensity. In the later trials, after the running response had been well learned, the running speeds were at about the same high level for all three shock groups. Extending this, it seems reasonable to say that the rate of acquisition of any response which is instrumental in terminating aversive stimulation (be it running away, simple bar pressing in a Skinner box, or a complex social behavior) is generally a function of the intensity of the aversive event.

Avoidance Behavior

This class of behavior is similar to that generated under escape conditions, the major difference being that the subject's response delays the occurrence of a noxious event instead of terminating it. Thus, as outlined earlier, an organism might be subjected to conditions under which he has to make a response every 10 seconds in order to prolong the absence of shock. Should the subject delay more than this period before responding, the aversive event occurs. Aside from the obvious factor of shock intensity, the amount of delay allowed is a critical variable here. Intuitively it probably strikes the reader that faster rates of responding are produced as the response-shock interval is decreased. This is indeed what was found with rhesus monkeys on a simple lever-pressing response (Sidman, et al., 1962) and with human subjects working a more complex monitoring task (Frazier, 1966).

Conditioned Emotional Behavior

Although the behavioral effects of simple escape or avoidance learning may appear to be obvious, a considerable degree of complexity occurs when a neutral stimulus is consistently paired with the aversive event. As indicated earlier, under these conditions the neutral stimulus acquires aversive properties itself. This phenomenon has been studied in a variety of forms, each of which is reviewed in this section.

Conditioned Avoidance. A classic experiment in this area was performed by Miller in 1948. The apparatus consisted of a two-compartment, rectangular box with an opening connecting the two sides of the box. One side was painted white and had a grid floor through which electric shocks could be delivered. The other side, painted black, had a wooden floor. In the first portion of the procedure, a rat was placed on the white side and given painful shock which he could escape by going through the doorway into the black compartment. During this preliminary escape training, note that several neutral stimuli were also being consistently paired with the electric shock, i.e., the color white and the grid floor. According to the paradigm, these neutral stimuli should acquire aversive properties; moreover, on subsequent trials, the rat should work to escape from them alone. Miller was able to demonstrate successfully just this. In a second portion of the experiment, the situation was changed. The shock was turned off and a sliding door was locked in place in the opening connecting the compartments. This door could be opened by the rat rotating a small wheel near the door. This the majority of the subjects learned to do. In other words, the previously neutral stimuli served as adequate cues for the learning of the new escape response.

Much subsequent work has been done on this model, and the reader is referred to Brown (1961) or Church (1963) for more detailed reviews. Several additional points are of interest, however, in this context. Solomon and Wynne (1953) have shown that these "fear-motivated" avoidance responses are particularly resistant to extinction. Thus, for example, rats who run to the black compartment might do so for hundreds of trials even though they never get shocked. Presumably, these subjects do not remain in the original learning situation (the white compartment) long enough so that extinction can take place. In addition, there is suggestive evidence that, if the rat is punished (shocked) *after* he makes the avoidance response (i.e., in the black compartment), the extinction process will be even slower (Brush, 1957). Quite possibly, this paradoxical effect can be accounted for by the fact that the punishment of the avoidance response reintroduces an important condition that was present during the original learning of the response (i.e., shock); hence the organism more persistently carries out the only response that he has learned in the situation—running through the doorway into the black compartment.

Several theorists have pointed out that this conditioned avoidance model can also be used to understand human fears and clinical phobias. The well-known demonstration by Watson and Raynor in 1920 was probably the first attempt at this application. By consistently pairing a loud, startling sound with the sight of a rabbit, these investigators were able to produce a conditioned fear response in a child at the sight of the rabbit alone. Moreover, the child also showed fear of other objects which were similar to the rabbit. More recently, Wolpe (1963) has successfully utilized an extension of this model in therapeutic efforts with phobias. By gradually exposing the phobic patient to stimuli which approximate more and more closely the feared object, he, in effect, "desensitizes" the patient. At the same time, the patient is taught to relax in the presence of these stimuli, thus producing a situation in which a response that is incompatible with the fear reaction (relaxation) is gradually substituted for the older, phobic response.

Conditioned Suppression. This related paradigm, also involving conditioning, was introduced in 1941 by Estes and Skinner. In the usual conditioned suppression design, the subject is taught to make a response (e.g., bar pressing for a rat) on the basis of positive reinforcement. By making this reinforcement occur only intermittently, a relatively steady rate of responding is produced. Following these preliminary procedures the suppression procedure is introduced. At points during responding, a neutral stimulus is presented (e.g., a tone) which remains on for a short length of time (e.g., one minute). At the cessation of the stimulus a noxious event (e.g., electric shock) occurs momentarily. After several of these, there is a marked drop in response rate during the tone-shock interval. This suppression effect is remarkably stable, although its magnitude varies with the intensity of both the conditioned stimulus (e.g., tone) and the unconditioned stimulus (e.g., shock) (Annau and Kamin, 1961; Kamin and Schaub, 1963).

This stability has made the conditioned suppression paradigm a useful tool with which to evaluate the effects of other procedures on emotional behavior. Thus, once the subject is displaying a reliable suppression effect, the influence of such procedures as electroconvulsive shock, drugs, or lesions in various portions of the brain can be examined. Hunt and Brady (1951) found, for example, that electroconvulsive shock "therapy" temporarily abolished the conditioned fear response (suppression) in rats.

Aversive Stimulation and Aggressive Behavior

As implied earlier in this chapter, the effects of aversive stimulation are not limited to behavioral suppression or withdrawal. In the escape or avoidance paradigm, for example, it is entirely possible to set up a situation in which the response that terminates or delays the noxious event will be a relatively complex set of social behaviors. Within this context a considerable amount of research on the development of aggressive behavior has been carried out.

Instrumental Aggression. Probably the most well-known demonstration of the relationship between aversive stimulation and aggression was published by Miller in 1948. Pairs of laboratory rats were placed in a small chamber and were electrically shocked. The shock remained on until the rats happened to assume aggressive postures toward each other, at which point the shock was terminated. Here, then, these rudimentary aggressive responses were instrumental in escaping the aversive stimulation. A short time later the shock was introduced again and remained on until the rats engaged in a somewhat higher degree of aggressive behavior. In this way the subjects were gradually "shaped" into full-blown fighting behavior.

Thus it seems reasonable to suggest that much of human aggression is developed and maintained on the same basis. That is to say, people learn that, under certain circumstances, aggression is an effective way of terminating noxious social stimulation. Support for this viewpoint comes from part of the data collected by Hokanson, et al. (1968) who used human subjects. Young adult subjects who were normally nonaggressive were placed in an interaction with an aggressive, punitive experimental accomplice. By prearrangement, the accomplice was programmed to become more friendly if the subject started to behave in a more aggressive manner. After a relatively short period, the subjects manifested a marked increase in aggressive behaviors.

Pain-Elicited Aggression. In the previous discussion it was shown how aggressive behavior could be utilized to terminate or delay aversive social stimulation. Perhaps more basic is the observation that the receipt of painful stimulation in itself produces aggression when an appropriate target is present. This phenomenon has been reliably observed in a variety of species ranging all the way from rats to monkeys (Ulrich, et al., 1965). Although the degree of pain-elicited fighting seems to depend on such variables as shock intensity, size of the enclosure housing the two animals, etc., it is interesting to note that the organism's prior reinforcement history with respect to aggression makes little difference. The phenomenon occurs whether the laboratory animal has been reared in community cages or in isolation (where, of course, there would be little opportunity for fighting behavior to be developed or reinforced) (Hutchinson et al., 1965). This has led most investigators in this area to suggest that this form of aggressive response to pain is unconditioned or "reflexive" (Ulrich and Azrin, 1962).

In terms of the earlier discussion of punishment, pain-elicited fighting has some interesting implications. It seems likely, for example, that, although punishment might effectively suppress other forms of behavior, this aversive stimulation might also increase the amount of aggressive responding. In the realm of child-rearing practices, then, a strong question concerning the over-all utility of punishment as a training device can be raised.

PHYSIOLOGICAL RESPONSES TO AVERSIVE STIMULATION

The physiology of pain has historically been difficult to specify. Many investigators (e.g., von Frey, 1895) have treated pain as a purely sensory phenomenon, largely ignoring its emotional and motivational aspects. This limited approach does not appear to do justice to a very complex and far-reaching pattern of events within the body. Moreover, a study of the relationship between these physiological events and the pain-motivated behavior described in the first section of this chapter has typically been by-passed, thus producing an artificial schism in this literature. Fortunately, in recent years a start has been made in developing a unified picture of the physiological-behavioral response to aversive stimulation. The work of Melzack and his group of investigators has been at the forefront of this new approach; hence their contributions form the core of this section.

Taking an overview of an organism's response to aversive stimulation, it is possible to delineate at least three areas of concern: (a) the sensory-discriminative; (b) the evaluative-cognitive; and (c) the motivational-affective (Melzack and Wall, 1965). This approach thus recognizes that pain is more than just a sensory-discriminative experience which merely detects the locality, intensity, and other immediate properties of the aversive stimulation. It also includes the associated emotional responses, the motivational qualities which impel the organism to make avoidance or other pain-reducing responses, and the evaluation made of the stimulation in terms of past experience and present context. This analysis of the phenomenon, although still vague, has an intuitive reasonableness about it, but which, of course, requires a great deal of documentation. It is the purpose of this section to outline the various physiological systems which underlie these multifaceted processes.

The Sensory-Discriminative System

Under this topic we are talking only about the physiological processes which detect and record the specific, immediate aspects of the aversive stimulation, not how this stimulation is interpreted or reacted to emotionally. As noted previously, the sensory-discriminative system has historically received the most attention and, thus, its circuitry is fairly well known. Strong stimulation of the skin evokes impulses in nerves which proceed toward the spinal cord (Figure 7.1). These sensory fibers approach the cord at the *dorsal root* and divide before reaching the cord. One bundle of fibers (large, myelinated, and fast) goes to the *dorsal-*

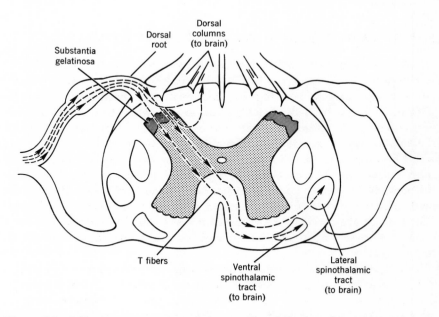

Figure 7.1 Schematic cross section of the spinal cord showing the incoming sensory impulses in the dorsal root which then take various routes to the brain.

column tract of the spinal cord which projects directly to the brain. For the moment let us delay further consideration of this dorsal-column route. We shall return to it when a closer look is taken at Melzack's theory. Of more immediate concern is the other bundle of fibers (small, unmyelinated, and slow) which takes a more circuitous route, impinging on a mass of cells in the dorsal horn of the spinal cord, known as the *substantia gelatinosa*. This mass, in turn, influences the first central transmission (T) cells in the *dorsal horn*. These second-order neurons cross the cord and then project to the brain via the *spinothalamic tracts*. These spinothalamic projections have been studied in some detail and are considered part of the *classical sensory system* for pain.

With respect to the sensory-discriminative dimension of pain, the next relevant structure is the thalamus. When the projections from the spinothalamic pathways reach this portion of the brain, they terminate in the *posteroventral* nucleus. This area is interesting in that it appears to be topographically organized, i.e., one section seems to represent all sensory input from the legs, another from the arms, etc. This same type of topographical organization is highly apparent in the subsequent cortical projections (in the postcentral area). Here, very detailed mapping of the cortex has been carried out (Woolsey, 1952) demonstrating the exquisite localization of somesthetic-sensory areas with corresponding parts of the body.

With this brief review of the important structures involved in sensing aversive stimulation, it is now possible to take a closer look at an important aspect of Melzack's theory. It is well known that there are many factors influencing the experience of pain. Such conditions as fear, expectation of pain, hypnotic suggestion, evaluation of the situation, and prior conditioning, to mention but a few, all have an influence. Such processes are usually considered to be mediated by the higher central-nervous-system structures (e.g., the frontal cortex). For example, men who are very seriously wounded in battle and withdrawn from the front lines may report little sense of pain from their wounds (although physiologically they should have been in great pain). At the same time they might complain bitterly about a clumsy puncture of a vein when getting medication (Beecher, 1959). In some way, then, the wounded mens' perception and evaluation of the over-all situation (being withdrawn from the front lines) affected their sensations of pain. Many other such paradoxical phenomena have been reported in the literature (Melzack and Casey, 1967). Hence the question: How do these higher cortical events affect the experience of pain?

In rough outline, Melzack proposes the following as part of his intriguing theory of pain.

The Evaluative-Cognitive System

We have already reviewed the fact that the main *sensory* information concerning aversive stimulation is carried by the relatively slow-conducting spinothalamic-thalamic-sensory cortical system. However, it will be recalled that neural information from the site of stimulation is also carried via the fast-conducting dorsal columns. It is this latter, early arriving information, according to Melzack, which is evaluated, compared with other sensory information, and interpreted in terms of past experience and present context in the higher central-nervous-system structures. Is it possible that these cortical events can now have a return effect on the sensory-discriminative information coming in on the classical pain pathways?

Melzack points out that there is ample evidence indicating that the frontal cortex can inhibit or modulate neural information coming in over the slow-conducting spinothalamic systems. Cortical events have been shown to inhibit electric impulses throughout this classical sensory pathway, all the way from the posteroventral nucleus of the thalamus (Shimazu et al., 1965) down to one of the earliest stages of the system—the dorsal horns of the spinal cord (Hagbarth and Kerr, 1954). It seems entirely likely, therefore, that, under some of the specialized environmental circumstances mentioned previously, the neural system carrying the primary pain information can be modulated by cortical events so that the input is markedly changed by the time it reaches the higher "pain" areas of the brain. Perhaps an everyday example will help to clarify this phenomenon. Consider a rather formal dinner party where the hostess hands you a very hot cup of coffee. Although painful, you have "presence of mind" not to drop the very expensive cup and you tolerate the burning sensation until, via some very gingerly adjustment, the cup can be placed down. The knowledge of the social consequences involved in breaking a piece of expensive china seems to have made the pain more tolerable.

The Motivational-Affective System

We have thus far looked at the purely sensory aspects of pain, and how these physical sensations can be affected by our interpretation of the over-all situation in which the aversive stimulation is encountered. Let us now look at a third aspect of pain, having to do with our emotional responses and their motivating properties.

As mentioned earlier, Melzack's argument for a consideration of the motivational-emotional dimension of pain seems entirely reasonable. It does not take very detailed introspection to recognize that in our personal experiences with aversive stimulation there are frequently degrees of emotional reaction as well as qualities of the experience which compel some sort of behavior to rid ourselves of the pain.

There is considerable evidence, much of it already reviewed in this book, which indicates that the reticular formation, the hypothalamus, and the limbic system are the primary areas of the brain subserving these motivational and emotional phenomena. It will also be recalled that these three brain areas are interconnected with each other and each, in turn, has fiber systems linking it with the cortex.

Electrical stimulation of many areas within these systems, particularly the limbic (e.g., hippocampus or amygdala; see Delgado, 1955, and Chapter VIII) produces fearlike responses and escape behavior. Stretching a point somewhat, it is as if the experimental animal were undergoing a severely painful stimulus at external sites on the body. By the same token, if many of these same brain areas are surgically ablated, there is a decrease in pain-related responsiveness. This type of evidence points to the limbic-hypothalamic-reticular system as the primary axis underlying the motivational and emotional dimension of pain. It is beyond the scope of this book to go into detail about the specific structures involved in each of these areas; however, the interested reader is referred to Brady (1958) for more thorough coverage.

It is of interest to recall the material presented in Chapter II on the topic of arousal. Mention was made of the fact that all sensory systems (including those for pain) send fibers to the reticular formation which, in turn, produces increased and generalized electrical activity in the higher brain centers, particularly in the cortex. Recall also the control exerted by the hypothalamus over both the autonomic nervous system and the hormones of the body (via the pituitary gland). Thus the complex circuitry of the limbic-hypothalamic-reticular system has ramifications throughout the body, affecting such processes as blood pressure, heart rate, blood sugar level, secretion of the hormone adrenalin from the adrenal medulla and a variety of steroids from the adrenal cortex, to mention a few. In short, virtually the entire internal environment (and particularly those physiological responses usually labeled *emotional*) is intimately tied in with the motivational-affective areas of the brain.

The role of the autonomic nervous system (ANS) in subserving motivational-affective phenomena bears further elaboration. In contrast to the central nervous system (CNS) and its peripheral fibers which control striated muscle and conduct sensory information, the ANS controls and modulates activity in the viscera (smooth muscle, glands, internal organs, the heart and lungs). As such it plays an important role in regulating these bodily processes, particularly in response to increases or decreases in the physical demands placed on the body. The ANS can be subdivided into two major systems—the sympathetic (SNS) and the parasympathetic (PNS)—with nerve fibers of the SNS leaving the spinal cord in the middle (thoracolumbar) regions, and fibers of the PNS emanating from the upper and tail ends (craniosacral regions).

SNS fibers exiting the spinal cord traverse a short distance before forming junctions (synapses). In this system, these synapses occur in groups, called *ganglia,* and SNS ganglia are interconnected, forming a sort of chain adjacent to the spinal cord. From here, postganglionic fibers of considerable length eventuate in the target organs. The high degree of interconnection between the SNS ganglia means that activity in the sympathetic system tends to be diffuse and mass-acting, i.e., stimulation of controlling centers in the brain, for example, produces effects throughout the system and tends to affect most of the target organs. In contrast, the PNS fibers leaving the spinal cord traverse relatively long distances and enter ganglia near the target organs. From there, short, postganglionic fibers terminate in the target organs. The relative absence of interconnections between PNS fibers and ganglia means that effects in this system tend to be more specific and limited to the organ being innervated.

Another important difference between the sympathetic and parasympathetic systems is at the biochemical level. SNS fibers, in most instances, stimulate target organs with noradrenalin (an adrenergic substance similar to secretions of the adrenal medulla). On the other hand, PNS innervation of target organs is via the cholinergic substance, acetylcholine. Of most immediate interest is the sympathetic-adrenergic relationship, which produces effects such as increased heart rate, increased blood pressure, etc., similar to those elicited when increased adrenalin output from the adrenal medulla begins to circulate through the blood stream. Here, then, is another factor leading to the widespread effects of SNS activity, because sympathetic processes typically produce increased secretions by the adrenal medulla.

From an adaptive point of view, the mass-acting effects of SNS activity make biological sense. The sympathetic system in general serves to support increased metabolic needs, physical activity, and sensory processes, and, as such, has frequently been viewed as serving "emergency" functions. Under threat or pain the organism, in effect, prepares to "fight" or "take flight." The pattern of physical changes taking place under these circumstances seems to fulfill these functions. Among the most significant changes which occur are the following: arteries serving large muscles (those needed for physical exertion) dilate, thus increasing their blood supply; blood vessels going to the digestive tract and to the periphery constrict; blood pressure, heart rate, and the heart stroke volume increase; in all, producing a pattern of vascular changes which would support intense or violent action. Similarly, respiration becomes fast and deep, bronchioles in the lungs dilate, and respiratory mucus decreases, all tending to make more oxygen available to the organism. The pupils of the eyes dilate, the EEG pattern reflects an arousal pattern, and behavioral alertness increases, again a pattern supportive of improved perceptual abilities. Finally, adrenalin (epinephrine) is secreted by the adrenal medulla which, circulating through the blood stream, enhances all of the foregoing effects and which also releases stores of sugar in the liver (thereby providing a rapid source of energy).

The parasympathetic system seems to have effects opposite to that of the SNS, and in the functioning organism the two systems operate to counterbalance one another. PNS predominance can best be seen in sleep, where heart rate and blood pressure are at lowered levels and vascular supply to the digestive tract is increased. Digestive processes are increased and sugar (glycogen) is stored in the liver. In sum, the PNS processes are replenishing in character.

A major degree of control of the autonomic nervous system resides in certain areas of the hypothalamus—an anatomically interesting fact, considering the central role played by this structure in other motivational systems and its integrating role with respect to the major hormonal systems. The posterior portion of the hypothalamus, when stimulated, elicits the whole array of SNS effects and seems to be a central station in the arousal process. (Recall also that this area was implicated in the metabolic response to cold and as a "wake" center in the research on sleep, again processes that fundamentally involve relatively high metabolic rates, energy expenditure, and behavioral arousal.) The PNS, on the other hand, is influenced strongly by the anterior hypothalamus (in terms of our earlier discussions, an area involved in heat dissipation and lowered metabolic rate).

In terms of our discussion of pain, it is not surprising to find that considerable research effort has involved the recording of autonomic processes in response to aversive stimulation. Such measures as heart rate or respiration are relatively easy to obtain and have been used to serve as an indicant of the broader sympathetic arousal within the organism. Although there are many technical and measurement problems inherent in interpreting autonomic data (many pertaining to the marked individual differences in these processes), this approach seems to have been a fruitful one in the study of physical responses to aversive events or threats of such.

Coming back to the motivational-affective dimension of pain, we see then that virtually the entire physiology of the organism may be mobilized to some degree by aversive stimulation. What remains is a discussion of the classical pain pathways and their relationships to the brain areas most intimately connected with the motivational-affective system associated with pain.

The sensory input concerning pain from the spinal cord sends collateral fibers to the limbic-hypothalamic-reticular system, thus providing access to the highly complex set of processes described previously. Melzack's argument, that pain is more than just a sensory experience, takes on more meaning when we see that the neural circuitry activated by aversive stimulation includes these motivational-emotional areas of the brain. Moreover, there is evidence (Bell et al., 1964) that the input into these areas is not topographically organized as is the thalamic and cortical projection system. Rather, Melzack theorizes that the limbic-hypothalamic-reticular areas merely detect the intensity of stimulation but provide little information concerning the site or the quality of the aversive stimulation. Inputs from virtually all sensory systems seem to funnel into this area where they all summate to produce an over-all level of activity. Furthermore, when the intensity of neural activity in this system reaches some critical threshold value, Melzack suggests that a behavioral action system is triggered, which is represented by learned and unlearned behavioral responses attempting to protect the organism from the aversive stimulation.

There is evidence in support of this last assertion from the work of Olds and Olds (1965). There are many areas within the limbic system and hypothalamus, which, if stimulated with low-intensity current, seem to have a reinforcing effect. That is, the organism with a permanently implanted electrode into one of these sites will work (e.g., press a bar) merely to receive electrical stimulation. One of the most potent of these "positive reinforcement" areas is the lateral hypothalamus (Olds and Olds, 1965). This material will be reviewed in the next chapter. For the moment, suffice it to point out that researchers have also found that, at certain electrode sites, if the intensity of the current is gradually increased, a point is reached in many of these sites where the electrical stimulation is no longer reinforcing. It now appears to become progressively more aversive and produces both defensive behaviors and painlike emotional responses.

Summary

The point of view proposed here is that, in order to appreciate the phenomenon of pain, three interrelated physiological systems need to be considered:

1. The classical sensory pathway to the brain which includes the spinothalamic tracts in the spinal cord, the posteroventral nucleus of the

thalamus, and the somatosensory area of the cortex. It is this system which carries the specific, detailed, and topographically organized information from the site of aversive stimulation to the sensory area of the cortex which "records" this information.

2. Other brain areas which presumably mediate thought and cognitive activity, wherein the sensory information concerning the aversive stimulation is compared with previous experiences of a similar nature and evaluated in terms of the over-all present situation. This system appears then to be capable of exerting a modulating effect on the neural firing in the classical sensory pathways, either decreasing or enhancing the electrical activity which eventually reaches the sensory cortex, depending on the situation.

3. In addition, the limbic-hypothalamic-reticular system receives neural fibers from the classical sensory pathways and seems to act as an "intensity monitor." When neural activity in these areas goes beyond some threshold level, there is an apparent triggering of autonomic, hormonal, and central-nervous-system events which can be described as an emotional response, *and* which set off the neural circuits eliciting overt instrumental behaviors protecting the organism or providing a means of escape.

Undoubtedly, these three systems interact with each other and provide many more complex inhibiting or enhancing effects. Again, it is beyond the scope of this presentation to review these issues; however, it should be instructive to conclude with a little speculation on the relationship between the physiological events described above and the learning phenomena covered in the first half of this chapter.

PHYSIOLOGICAL AND BEHAVIORAL RESPONSES TO AVERSIVE STIMULATION

As with most of the other topics dealt with in this book, we ultimately arrive at a blank spot—a place where relatively little is scientifically known. Consider the material presented in this chapter thus far. Although much more experimentation is needed, a considerable body of knowledge has been accumulated on the behavioral (learned) effects of aversive stimulation. The same statement can be made about the physiological processes that occur with pain. Practically nothing, however, is known about how the physiological events are translated into the behavioral events. Thus when a rat in a Skinner box receives a severe electric shock to the foot pads, we can with considerable accuracy detail the chain of physiological events from the electrical response in the peripheral nerves all the way up to the sensory cortex and other brain areas. Similarly, the variables affecting the learned behaviors of pressing the bar to turn off the shock have been reasonably well documented. The absent link in the chain is a description of the processes taking place when the sensory events (pain) activate the motor responses involved in making the escape or avoidance responses.

James and Marianne Olds (1965) have recently published some ideas on this general issue which bear consideration. First, however, it will be necessary to review two anatomical points briefly.

1. The pyramidal and the extrapyramidal fiber tracts are the primary *motor* systems projecting "downward" from the cortex to the skeletal system of the organism, i.e., activity in these systems controls overt movement and postural responses.

2. As indicated earlier, the lateral hypothalamus, in addition to being a basic eating and drinking center, is also one of the prime "reinforcement" areas of the brain, i.e., an organism will work to receive low-level electrical stimulation to this area.

In the view of Olds and Olds, this lateral hypothalamic area assumes greater importance because they consider it a site of convergence of many of the "reinforcement" and "aversive" areas of the brain. Thus this "final common path" represents an area where interaction between aversive and positively reinforcing neural events may take place.

Interestingly enough, the motor fibers (pyramidal and extrapyramidal tracts) described previously pass through the lateral hypothalamic area, with many short collateral fibers offering opportunity for interaction between the two systems. Is it possible then, asks Olds, that reinforcing or aversive events which ultimately produce neural changes in the lateral hypothalamic area can, in turn, produce changes in the motor fibers that govern overt behavior? Although still not clearly documented, they report some preliminary data (Olds and Olds, 1961) which support this notion. They recorded the rate of neural firing from single fibers in the motor system. Then an attempt was made to condition operantly this firing rate by using low-level electrical stimulation to the lateral hypothalamus as the reinforcer. This was tried in both directions; i.e., reinforce after motor-system firing temporarily stopped, thereby attempting to reduce operantly the firing rate, and, secondly, to reinforce increases in firing rate. In several of their preparations they reported successful demonstrations of this operant control, but technical problems of microelectrode placement, etc., precluded completely clear-cut results. Nevertheless, the fact that they could apparently control the electric discharge in these motor fibers by *subsequent* stimulation in the lateral hypothalamus seems to be an extremely important start in gaining an understanding of basic physiological-behavioral relationships.

As a footnote it should be pointed out that the foregoing demonstration only deals with one small aspect of the controls on motor behavior. The problem of how complex sequences of learned, coordinated, and directed motor patterns are physiologically determined is still many years from being solved.

THE CONCEPT OF STRESS

Our emphasis thus far in this chapter has been on the behavioral and physiological concomitants of physically painful stimulation. In a sense, by looking at the neurological substrate of the experience of pain and the immediate behavioral reaction to that experience, a relatively narrow view of the concept of aversiveness has been developed. To be sure, events other than physical pain per se are experienced as aversive; moreover, the organism's response to aversive events frequently goes beyond just an immediate and specific adaptive reaction to the noxious stimulus. It becomes necessary then to deal with two additional issues: (a) to catalogue and discuss stimuli and situations other than physical pain as to their aversive properties and (b) to describe some of the broader, nonspecific reactions to aversive stimulation that have been investigated. In this context the term *stress* will be used in its most general sense, to denote any pattern of stimulation which the organism finds obnoxious, seeks to avoid, or to which he displays behaviors generally agreed upon as reflecting negative emotions.

In a major review of the general area of stress, Lazarus (1966) suggests that research efforts can be logically divided into two broad categories: (a) descriptions of the types of situations which are stressful and (b) analyses of the reactions to stress. Under the second heading, the research data can be further subdivided into reports of disturbed emotions, effects on motor behaviors, changes in the adequacy of cognitive functioning, and physiological changes.

Stimulus, Situational, and Individual Factors

The concept of stress has been studied extensively both in the laboratory and in naturalistic circumstances. Many provocative insights into the nature of stress have been obtained by interviews and observations of people who have undergone natural or man-made disasters—insights which have then been more specifically investigated under controlled laboratory conditions.

One of the most obvious situational stress factors to have been studied in natural settings is the confrontation with potentially harmful circumstances. Important works in this area include several studies of men in combat (Grinker and Spiegel, 1945; Janis, 1951; Tompkins, 1959); persons in concentration or POW camps (Bettelheim, 1960; Farber et al., 1957); reactions to natural disasters such as floods and tornadoes (Janis, 1962); anticipation of surgery (Janis, 1958); and responses before, during, and after dangerous activities such as parachute jumping (Epstein, 1962).

Lazarus (1966) points out that several general factors related to the intensity of stress can be derived from these works. Foremost, and perhaps most obvious, is the generalization that the greater the objective danger or the more imminent the danger, the greater the stress reaction among those involved. Tompkins (1959), for example, found that the incidence of clinical neuroses among combat pilots rose as the nature of assignments became more dangerous. Epstein (1962) demonstrated that subjective feelings of distress and autonomic signs of arousal progressively increased among parachutists as the time for the actual jump approached. As might be expected, countless laboratory studies (of course, using considerably milder forms of aversive stimulation) offer support for this generalization (see earlier behavioral section of this chapter).

Perhaps more interesting are the effects of prior experience and individual difference factors in response to potentially stressful circumstances. Several recurrent themes run through the accounts of combat veterans and victims of disaster. An evaluation of "dangerous" is frequently not made until the individual has had some first-hand experience with a particular situation. For example, novices on combat missions reported a kind of detached interest in flak bursts upon their first encounter; it was not until they actually saw an adjoining plane being hit or a friend wounded by shrapnel that the awesomeness of the situation struck home (Grinker and Spiegel, 1945). Along similar lines, Danzig et al. (1958) found that approximately 90% of the people who displayed panic behavior and attempted to flee in response to rumors of a possible flood were those who had previously undergone experiences with an earlier flooding of their area. Evidently, then, the impact of cues signaling danger and the consequent behavioral response to those cues are enhanced by prior experience in similar situations (Lazarus, 1966). An interesting laboratory analog of this process is provided in a study by Lindzey et al. (1960) in which infant mice were exposed to very loud, high-frequency noise. This infantile "trauma" had marked effects on later behaviors in similar environments, wherein the traumatized rats showed heightened signs of emotionality, fearfulness, and timidity.

A second individual difference factor encountered in field studies of stress is that stress reactions are heightened when effective behaviors to deal with potential danger are not available. One of the most direct demonstrations of this effect with humans is the study by Epstein (1962) in which the emotional and autonomic reactions of experienced and inexperienced parachutists were compared. The experienced jumpers, presumably with greater skills and practice at the task, showed only moderate levels of physiological arousal in the period leading up to the jump, whereas inexperienced subjects displayed intense activation. That this relationship is more complex, however, is suggested by another facet of Epstein's findings. With extensive parachuting experience, arousal again becomes heightened in the actual jumping situation, quite possibly because the jumper assumes that with repeated attempts his luck will run out.

An elaboration of the relationship between heightened distress and the unavailability of effective countermeasures to stress is illustrated most tragically in Bettelheim's (1960) account of the organization of Nazi concentration camps. The camp procedures were arranged so that all individual initiative among prisoners was suppressed to the degree that inmates acquired the feeling that every aspect of their existence was under external control by the guards. Official camp policies even went so far as to make whipping the penalty for unsuccessful suicide attempts, thus in a sense attempting to control even the ultimate choice of one's fate. Comparable procedures were utilized in North Korean POW camps as part of the brainwashing technique (Farber et al., 1957).

A laboratory study which illustrates the relationship between prior experience, effective counterbehaviors, and physiological stress reactions is provided by Hokanson, et al. (1968). Subjects underwent a series of encounters with a consistently punitive and aggressive experimental accomplice; with each encounter they displayed a marked increase in vascular arousal, followed by a very slow return of vascular processes to normal levels. In a subsequent phase of the experiment, subjects were "taught" a behavior that was an effective means of reducing the accomplice's punitiveness. Following this learning procedure, subjects now utilized the newly learned counterbehavior to cope with the interpersonal stress and, concomitantly, showed very rapid reductions in vascular arousal when they were stressed.

The fact that effective defensive behaviors need not necessarily be overt is illustrated in a series of studies by Lazarus (Lazarus et al., 1965). In these experiments it was demonstrated that a subject's "cognitive appraisal" (comparable to Melzack's evaluative-cognitive dimension) of a potentially stressful situation had appreciable effects on his verbal and autonomic responses. Subjects viewed a film which depicted a series of rather gruesome shop accidents. Several of the incidents were presented so that the viewer could anticipate the gory accident, and, as might be expected, these sequences were accompanied by progressively heightened signs of autonomic arousal. However, when some subjects were given defensive orientations prior to viewing the film, these autonomic indicants of disturbance were greatly reduced during the presentation of the film. These orientations were modeled after the psychoanalytic defenses of denial (emphasizing that, after all, it was only a dramatic film) and intellectualization (stressing the implications for shop safety in the film). Thus these orientations represented different ways to evaluate a complex set of stimuli and had demonstrable effects on subjects' physiological reactions to the stressors.

Aside from such factors as the objective danger, imminence of possible harm, individual differences in mode of appraisal, and the availability of coping behaviors, Lazarus (1966) also cites *ambiguity of stimulus cues* as an important determinant of stress reactions. Presumably stress is enhanced in potentially threatening situations by ambiguity, because the individual is less able to invoke defensive behaviors or to predict clearly the nature of the aversive events. Some support for this contention is offered by Dibner (1958) who conducted two forms of psychiatric interviews with neurotic patients. Half of the patients were exposed to an ambiguous interview where no cues were given as to what they were to talk about, whereas the others were given considerable structure. On a variety of stress measures, the patients in the ambiguous condition showed markedly heightened signs of disturbance relative to the "structured" group.

This last study points up an important consideration in this survey of situational factors which are stressful. In this situation, there was very little objective danger of physical harm. The "stress" here was presumably related to the subject's appraisal of himself or to his fears concerning the interviewer's evaluation of him. This type of "psychological stress" has been effectively demonstrated in a myriad of studies, and has involved such procedures as personal insult (Funkenstein et al., 1957), questioning a subject's intelligence (Hokanson and Burgess, 1962), social rejection (Vogel, et al., 1959), showing disturbing movies (Lazarus, et al., 1962), and many variants of this type of "ego threat." Again, the effectiveness of these manipulations appears to be dependent on individual differences among subjects, with some of the more important personality factors being need for social approval (Conn and Crowne, 1964), anxiety proneness (Spence, 1958), test anxiety (Sarason and Mandler, 1952), defensive effectiveness (Wolff et al., 1964), and aggressiveness (Hokanson, 1961).

Summary

Taken as a whole, the extensive literature on the stimulus factors which can be defined as stressful presents a vastly complex array of problems.

Perhaps the central issue in this area is the finding that it is virtually impossible to define a set of stimuli as stressful on the basis of external factors alone. As pointed out earlier, in connection with Melzack's theory of pain, it appears that the individual's interpretation and appraisal of the stimuli plus his available coping behaviors are important determinants of whether or not a situation will be stressful. In this light, the study of historical and personality factors of individual subjects becomes of central concern in stress research. A second, related issue pertains to the methods used to measure whether a particular situation is stressful for a subject. Here again, marked individual differences occur in the manner in which subjects display their disturbances, ranging all the way from culturally learned patterns of facial expression and gestures (Efron and Foley, 1947) to idiosyncratic patterns of autonomic reactivity (Lacey and Lacey, 1958). Quite clearly, then, subject differences, both in terms of the appraisal of threatening circumstances and mode of expressing disturbances, run through the stress literature. Research problems connected with these issues are perhaps best exemplified in studies of the behavioral and cognitive effects of stress.

Nonspecific Behavioral and Cognitive Effects

As might be expected in view of the multiplicity of situational, individual differences, and measurement factors found in stress research, no easy generalizations concerning behavioral effects are possible. Hence this section is designed merely to point up some of the major research efforts and some of the problems encountered. Two main areas will be touched upon: stress effects on nonspecific motor responding and effects on intellectual behaviors.

Motor Behavior. Viewing motor behavior at a general level, there appears to be reasonably good evidence that stress is associated with increased vigor of motor responding. Support for this contention comes from a large number of studies in a variety of areas. Increased tremors (Luria, 1932), elevated muscle potentials (Malmo et al., 1951), enhanced vigor of a manual response (Haner and Brown, 1955), and faster running speeds (Amsel and Ward, 1954) have all been observed in response to one form of stress or another. These types of findings have led a number of behavior theorists to suggest that stress (or specific variants of it such as frustration) contributes to the general drive level of the organism (Brown and Farber, 1951; Spence, 1958; Amsel, 1958). These extensions of Hullian theory maintain, therefore, that all potential responses of the organism are energized via this increased level of drive.

Although the effects of stress in enhancing the vigor of responding do not appear to be in serious dispute, a number of investigators have focused on the debilitating effects of stress. Maier (1956), for example, has argued that behavior following frustration or insoluble conflict becomes stereotyped, resistant to change, and maladaptive. These "neurotic" behaviors may evidently take various forms, such as "freezing" (Mowrer, 1940), paniclike running (Solomon and Wynne, 1953), stereotyped movement patterns (Maier, 1956), and reduced abilities to carry out instrumental behaviors (Brady and Hunt, 1955). In an interesting theoretical paper, Wilson (1963) points out the similarity between the aforementioned maladaptive behaviors induced in animals by experimental procedures and reaction patterns displayed by human clinical patients who have been diagnosed as neurotic. In general, it appears that these extreme forms of response to stress occur when the subject is placed in an inescapable and severe situation or when faced with a seemingly insoluble conflict. As we shall see in the next section, however, it would be incorrect to assume that all stress produces debilitating effects.

The general increase of motor responding under stress appears to be consistent with the findings concerning physiological processes which affect the motor systems of the body. Downward projections from the hypothalamus and reticular formation course through the interior grey stalk of the brain and spinal cord (tegmentum) and have widespread effects on motor reactivity (Crosby and Woodburn, 1951). In addition, epinephrine and norepinephrine, released during periods of threat, enhance motor functions; of course, the whole pattern of sympathetic effects (blood diverted to muscles, release of stored sugar, etc.) provides for the energy requirements of increased motor activity. Certainly, then, from a survival point of view, the physiological events which accompany stress seem to be patterned to aid the organism in coping motorically with potentially harmful situations.

Intellectual Functions. We now arrive at a topic which has an extensive experimental literature, but which also contains many inconsistent and conflicting findings. Basically the question being asked here concerns the effects of stress on cognitive behaviors, i.e., does it increase or decrease abilities to learn, discriminate, carry out complex problem-solving tasks, and other intellectual functions. As might be expected, no easy or simple answer is available, mainly because there are so many variables to be considered. As has already been alluded to, the intensity and type of stress, the subject's prior learning history, other personality factors, the availability of coping behaviors, and the nature of the task being performed are all critical factors in determining the effects of a stressor on intellectual performance. Extensive reviews of this literature are available (Lazarus, et al., 1952; Lazarus, 1966, Chapter 8).

Let us begin with some basic data from physiologically orientated work. In Chapter II, the role of the hypothalamus, reticular formation, visceral brain, cortex, and other structures were discussed with respect to the general arousal level of the organism. It also became apparent that inter-related processes in these portions of the brain have influences which go beyond the mere control of wakefulness or activation; in addition, they have effects on cortical patterns of electrical response, sensory input to higher brain centers, orienting responses toward selective portions of the environment, and general alertness to the external world. These processes of course, are basic aspects of one's cognitive functioning, and hence are critical in determining the quality and direction of interactions with the environment. The fact that these same areas of the brain are involved in the organism's response to dangerous circumstances provides a clear overlap between the experimental literature on stress and that dealing with general arousal.

Recall from the earlier discussion that Fuster (1958) and Ogowa (1963) found increased discrimination abilities with moderate intensities of stim-ulation to the reticular formation. Moreover, the former study showed that with intense reticular stimulation (strong enough to evoke overt signs of alarm) the subjects' abilities to discriminate between geometric forms decreased. These results can serve as a convenient reference point by which to analyze much of the experimental work done in the area of stress and intellectual performance.

As a first approximation to a generalization, it might be said that, if a subject is aroused from a state of relaxation or drowsiness to one of be-havioral alertness, there will most likely be an increase in efficiency of performance. This generalization appears to hold if the arousing stimulus is either innocuous or moderately threatening. For example, Wood and Hokanson (1965) found that intermediate levels of induced muscular effort (nonthreatening) produced increased efficiency on a clerical speed task. Similarly, Burgess and Hokanson (1968) found that with non-aroused subjects (as defined by low heart rates) a moderately stressful frustration experience also produced an increase in efficiency on the same task. Comparable findings have been obtained in earlier studies by Farber and Spence (1953), Lucas (1952), and Montague (1953) using paper and pencil tests to evaluate subjects' arousal (drive) levels. Thus there appears to be a reasonable amount of evidence in support of the notion that moderate levels of stress (given a reasonably nonaroused sub-ject to begin with) may facilitate performance on an intellectual task.

Admittedly, this view is an oversimplification of the problem. At least two important additional classes of variables need to be considered: characteristics of the subject and the nature of the intellectual task. With regard to the former, it appears that, if a subject is displaying a high level of arousal prior to the stress (as defined by either elevated autonomic processes or verbal report on a questionnaire), even moderately stressful stimulation will produce decrements in ongoing performance (Burgess and Hokanson, 1968; Montague, 1953; Doerr and Hokanson, 1965). For the moment, let us delay consideration of the theoretical implications of these findings other than to indicate that it appears that, once the arousal level of a subject goes beyond some critical level, behaviors which interfere with ongoing performance are evoked.

Characteristics of the cognitive task are also an important consideration in evaluating the effects of stress. When the task is relatively simple (i.e., the task itself does not elicit a variety of competing responses) or when the task involves primarily motor speed, stress-produced increases in arousal (or drive) seem to enhance performance (Hokanson and Burgess, 1964; Lucas, 1952). However, with more complex tasks (involving subtle discriminations or where a variety of responses are called for), the effects of stress are more variable, but, on the whole, produce decrements in task efficiency (Farber and Spence, 1953; Hokanson and Burgess, 1964). As might be expected, however, the more practice a subject has with a particular complex task, the less debilitating are the effects of a stressor (e.g., Fenz, 1964).

A number of theoretical positions have been presented to account for the phenomena discussed previously. Kenneth Spence and his associates at the University of Iowa attempted to develop an explanatory model based on the Hullian concept of drive (Spence, 1958), in which, it will be recalled from Chapter I, it was theorized that drive enhances the strengths of all habits. This applies to both correct and incorrect habits connected with a particular task. Thus, with an increase in drive level, the Spence position would predict an increase in the occurrence of both correct and incorrect responses during task performance. If the task is a simple one (not many competing, incorrect responses), an increase in drive level should enhance performance. However, with a complex task, heightened drive should strengthen both correct and a variety of wrong responses, thereby reducing performance efficiency. Although much of the existing data fit this model, the position has been questioned both on logical grounds and on the basis of inconsistent findings (Sarason, 1960).

An alternate, although not mutually exclusive, theoretical orientation suggests that stress arouses a variety of emotional responses (primarily anxiety), and that these task-irrelevant responses interfere or compete with behaviors necessary for adequate performance on the task (Child and Waterhouse, 1953; Sarason, et al., 1952). Easterbrook (1959) suggests that under threat the individual restricts his range of attention to cues related to danger and, thus, may not be oriented or attend to task-related cues. As described earlier, under more intense threat, such behaviors as freezing, crouching, or panic quite clearly are responses which under most circumstances would interfere with ongoing performance.

Although both the drive and the interference theories are general, they seem to complement the experimental findings in the arousal area. In addition, the notion that anxiety responses may compete with ongoing task behaviors finds a parallel in Melzack's conception of a central intensity monitor. Recall Melzack's suggestion that, when the arousal level (probably in the reticular formation) goes beyond a certain threshold, an emotional-motivational system is triggered which elicits behaviors designed to reduce aversiveness (Melzack and Wall, 1965). In a situation involving performance on a task, these defensive behaviors might well interfere with task-related activities.

Summary. Research on the effects of stress on performance has proved to be an exceptionally complex area, and it seems likely that no single theory will be adequate to encompass all the data at present. One major problem in the area is that investigators have used such a wide variety of stressors, tasks, and personality measures that comparisons across studies are very difficult to make. Secondly, little attempt has been made to quantify some of the important variables that are known to affect performance. For example, it is readily apparent that the intensity of stress is a critical factor and, yet, virtually no systematic attempts to scale this dimension have been made. Similarly, the task-complexity variable is in dire need of quantification, but as yet only minimal efforts in this direction are apparent (Hokanson and Burgess, 1964). Hence it seems that, in this area, theorizing is somewhat premature, and an adequate model of stress and performance relationships must await more precise, parametric data on all the pertinent variables.

Nonspecific Physiological Effects of Stress

As in the previous section, we shall see that much work remains to be done to clarify the physiology of stress. Upon reviewing the literature in this area we are struck by the fact that much of the existing research is compartmentalized and that few efforts have been made to organize systematically the experimental results. One major exception, however, is the work of Hans Selye who has carried out a program of research on the nonspecific physical effects of stress over the past 30 years (Selye, 1936, 1950, 1958). Hence this section begins with a general view of Selye's notions, to be followed by discussions of several important subissues in the field.

The General Adaptation Syndrome. Fundamental to Selye's view of stress is the observation that a noxious agent produces not only a specific bodily reaction (e.g., vasoconstriction to cold) but also a wide range of nonspecific physical changes. These nonspecific processes, which in Selye's view are relatively stereotyped for each individual, are the focus of his work. Extending Cannon's concept of homeostasis (1927), these wide-ranging physiological changes are viewed by Selye as the body's attempt to cope with stress when normal homeostatic and defensive behaviors have failed. Interestingly, these nonspecific stress responses have been found to occur not only with physical stressors, such as extreme thermal conditions, infection, physical injury, and X-irradiation, but also with social and interpersonal disturbances (Christian, 1959; Basowitz et al., 1955). Selye thereby provides a conceptual framework which appears to be general enough to incorporate a wide range of noxious events.

The stress responses, which Selye labels the *general adaptation syndrome,* follow a characteristic pattern that can be divided into three phases: (*a*) an initial *alarm reaction* upon first encountering the aversive stimulation; (*b*) a *stage of resistance,* in which the body's adaptive processes are in operation; and (*c*) an *exhaustion stage,* in which the adaptive functions no longer can be supported. Naturally, progression through these stages is dependent on how long the noxious agent is present. In addition, the processes may proceed directly from the stage of alarm to that of exhaustion, depending on the severity of the stressor and the state of the organism.

Selye divides the alarm reaction into two subphases: shock and countershock. The former is characterized by a wide array of autonomic and biochemical changes, such as secretion of epinephrine by the adrenal medulla, increases in the usual autonomic signs of arousal (heart rate, blood pressure, etc.), changes in sugar level, alkalinity and white corpuscle count in the blood, and the beginnings of processes leading to ulcerations in the gastrointestinal system. The second phase of the alarm reaction (countershock) represents the beginnings of a defensive adjustment to the stress and appears to be marked by the initiation of more prolonged hormonal and endocrine gland changes. Such processes as increased secretions by the adrenal medulla (epinephrine and norepinephrine), adrenal cortex (steroids), and thyroid (thyroxin, affecting general metabolism) are characteristic of this phase. These processes are, however, accompanied by other changes which, in effect, show the price the body is paying in coping with the stress. Enlargement of the adrenal glands, degenerative changes in lymph tissue, and further ulceration in the stomach and intestines are among the more important effects found.

During the stage of resistance, the body evidently is adapting to the altered set of physiological processes, and signs of distress do not appear to be as severe. However, again it is apparent that the prolonged stress takes its toll in that these adjustments eventually are replaced by the exhaustion stage wherein the symptoms of the alarm reaction return. Selye (1956) points out that the debilitation which takes place during exhaustion may well be partially caused by the unusual adaptive responses which occur during the resistance stage. That is, the altered biochemical processes found during the middle phase of the syndrome may actually be responsible for further tissue damage. For example, Selye (1956) reports that the administration of normally adaptive amounts of adrenal hormones to an organism already under stress can cause tissue damage in the heart, blood vessels, liver, and a variety of other organs. Thus he suggests that the very processes which apparently serve an adaptive function can, in turn, become stressors during prolonged periods of disturbance.

We have here, then, a set of observations and a general model pertaining to psychosomatic changes during both psychological and physical stress. Again, this scheme seems to represent a valid overview of long-term processes, but, as in our earlier discussions of stress, many specific issues have been left unanswered. For example, the ever-present observation of individual differences in susceptibility to stress is an important area of research, as is the question of the specific patterning of physiological responses to various stressors.

Individual Differences. There is reasonable evidence that individual differences in responsivity to stressors can at least be partially accounted for on the basis of genetic inheritance. For example, various traits of emotionality, shyness, and aggressiveness have been selectively bred into colonies of experimental animals (Hall, 1951; Scott and Charles, 1954). Similarly, there is some evidence that individual patterns of autonomic responding are affected by constitutional factors in humans (Lacey and Lacey, 1958). Thus, for example, physicians who are attempting to evaluate an individual's potential for heart disease will frequently inquire about histories of coronary problems in his family.

More interesting are individual differences which come about on the basis of life experiences. Here, however, the data tend to be inconsistent and no easy conclusions can be drawn. Selye (1958) suggests that there may be certain critical periods in an organism's development during which rather marked influences on later stress responses may be effected. If, for example, the organism is exposed to stress at an appropriate early stage, it may "immunize" him from stress effects later in life. Although an intriguing possibility, this hypothesis remains tentative, and there is some evidence which runs counter to it. Recall the study by Lindzey et al. (1960), in which they found that, for experimental mice, early trauma led to greater timidity and emotionality in later life. In addition, Selye (1958) found that early exposure to threat in conjunction with certain hormone treatments produced more severe stress reactions. It may well be that the direction of these effects is dependent on a complex interaction among stage of development, intensity, and temporal factors of the induced threat and the organism's ability to mobilize effective adaptive responses at the time of stress.

Patterning of Responses. Psychophysiologists and psychologists in recent years have devoted considerable effort to understand some of the factors affecting the manner in which autonomic responses react in relation to one another. Although it appears that during stress a general sympathetic arousal occurs, the more recent experimental emphasis has been on the *pattern* of autonomic discharge and its determinants. This interest grew out of some of the early theorizing within the field of psychosomatic medicine, in which it was thought that specific psychosomatic ailments (e.g., ulcers) were developed because of specific psychological conflicts.

John Lacey has provided much of the basic data in this area. As already mentioned, it appears that individuals tend to display the same pattern of autonomic response to a variety of different stressors (Lacey and Lacey, 1958). It seems likely that this *individual-response specificity* can account for some of the development of particular psychosomatic disorders under prolonged stress. Thus, for example, one individual's predominant autonomic response to stress may be manifested in marked changes in heart action, but little change in gastric motility or stomach secretions is observed. Another person may show just the opposite pattern. Aside from the implications of these types of results for psychosomatic developments, the reader might also consider the problems these individual patterns present for an experimenter who is merely trying to study a general autonomic response to stress. If the experimenter is only using one autonomic measure, he may well find that a number of his subjects show only a minimal response to a stressor. Considering Lacey's findings, it would, of course, be incorrect for the experimenter to conclude that these nonresponding subjects were not aroused.

We are also indebted to Lacey for an elaboration of the concept of *situational* or *stimulus specificity* (Lacey, et al., 1963). Here the findings have shown that particular stimulus situations evoke specific patterns of autonomic response. Perhaps here it would be more accurate to say that a subject's interpretation of a situation evokes particular patterns of response, because some investigators have demonstrated that subjective emotional reactions correlate with autonomic patterns.

Lacey et al. (1963) focused on the cardiac response to environmental stimulation and found that cardiac decelerations generally accompanied stimuli which the subject wanted to "take in" (e.g., see more of). On the other hand, stimuli which the subject wanted to "reject" (e.g., aversive stimulation) were associated with cardiac accelerations. There are some added implications in these findings that these cardiac responses may be, in turn, linked with sensory processes, so that, in effect, they may play an instrumental role in facilitating or inhibiting intake from the environment.

The patterning of autonomic responses has also been investigated in relation to subjectively experienced emotional states. Such investigators as Ax (1953) and Funkenstein et al. (1957) present evidence that the autonomic pattern during the experience of fear is different from that during states of anger. They suggest that the fear pattern is epinephrine-like, i.e., similar to the pattern obtained when epinephrine is injected into the blood stream. Concomitants of anger, however, have been termed *norepinephrine-like*. These inferences concerning the hormonal substrate of a particular autonomic pattern must necessarily be tentative; however, some attempts to measure directly the levels of these hormones during various stress episodes offer supporting evidence (Elmadjian, et al., 1958).

In conclusion, however, it should be pointed out that more complex aspects of the problem of autonomic patterning are involved. Levi (1965), for example, has observed that both epinephrine and norepinephrine levels were increased during the viewing of fear- and anger-provoking films and, more important, also during the viewing of a comic film which elicited positive emotions. This investigator thus suggests that the two hormones may be natural concomitants of emotionally arousing situations, regardless of whether they are aversive or not. Lastly, the work of Schachter and Singer (1962), in which they found that the experienced reaction to injections of these hormones was highly dependent on the subject's interpretation of the social setting, emphasizes again the cognitive-evaluative variables which ultimately seem to control responses to stress.

VIII

Some Motivational Effects
of Brain Stimulation

Perhaps the historically most persistent view on the nature of motivation is based on the concepts of pleasure and pain. From ancient Greek hedonistic thought to the social theories of such English philosophers as Hobbes (1588–1679) and Bentham (1748–1832), behavior was considered to be regulated so as to maximize pleasure and minimize pain. A significant dimension was added to this view through Herbert Spencer's extension of Darwinian theory (1880), wherein pleasurable activities were also thought to have "survival value," whereas pain was a signal that the organism's well-being was threatened. Living creatures, including humans, were thus viewed as continually adjusting to the environment in such a way as to achieve biological and personal satisfactions (survival) with minimum penalties or pain.

The concepts of pleasure and pain, referring to internal experiences of the organism, tended to be discarded with the rise of behaviorism during the 1920's. The vigorous emphasis on building a theory of behavior based on observable phenomena precluded the use of these subjective terms as motivational constructs. A more empirical emphasis can thus be noted in much of the more recent theorizing on the nature of motivation and reinforcement (Bolles, 1967); for our purposes, the contributions of Clark Hull (1943) and Neal Miller (1959) are the most important of the recent work.

Central to Hull's views on motivation was the concept of drive, which, in essence, was thought to be a reflection of the organism's tissue needs. Thus, for example, in the case of hunger, drive could be experimentally manipulated by regulating the number of hours of food deprivation to which an animal was subjected. These physiologically based drives were also assumed to produce characteristic drive stimuli—cues to the organism which reflected variations in the bodily conditions involved. Within this drive context, the notion of reinforcement (consequents which strengthen preceding behaviors) took on rather specific meaning, i.e., drive reduction is the basic process underlying reinforcement. In this way the concept assumed very definite physiological referents pertaining ultimately to the satisfaction of bodily needs of the organism. Miller and Dollard (1941) and Miller (1948) gave this viewpoint a slightly different and broader emphasis by suggesting that any strong stimulation, whether related to tissue depletion or not, can have drive (motivating) properties, and that the reduction of this strong stimulation defines the reinforcement concept. From these viewpoints, then, organisms were thought to work and/or learn new behaviors, and, ultimately, these behaviors or chains of behaviors eventuated in the restoration of physiological deficits and/or the reduction of strong stimulation.

This drive-reduction or stimulus-reduction point of view became one of the most influential theories relating learning and motivation during the 1940's and 1950's; in addition, it prompted a considerable amount of research and controversy. It is the purpose of this chapter to review some of the major issues which have arisen with respect to the drive-reduction viewpoint, with particular emphasis on research involving electrical stimulation of the brain. The chapter concludes with a summary of a recent attempt by Grossman (1967) to place the drive-reduction concept in a larger perspective of motivational phenomena.

REINFORCEMENT WITHOUT DRIVE REDUCTION

Let us begin this section with a working definition of a reinforcer as any stimulus for which the organism will work or learn a new behavior. From this point of view, there have been a substantial number of studies indicating that organisms will work for reinforcements which can hardly be considered to provide drive or stimulus reduction. As a matter of fact, the effective reinforcements here seem to be characterized by *increases* in stimulation. Perhaps the most dramatic example of this type of effect is provided by experiments in the area of "sensory deprivation" (Bexton, et al., 1954). Here college student volunteers were paid a considerable salary to spend 24 hours a day in an environment which permitted little sensory stimulation. Translucent goggles, special gloves, arm cuffs, and a sound-deadened room, among other devices, sharply reduced the amount of patterned visual, auditory, or tactile stimulation ordinarily received from the environment. After some initial sleeping, subjects found this experience to be extremely aversive. Judging from the subjects' reports, they almost began to crave stimulation and engaged in a variety of simple activities to promote sensations and eagerly looked forward to any form of environmental stimulation provided by the experimenters. Many subjects reported having hallucinatory experiences under these conditions. It was found that rarely could a subject tolerate the experiment for more than two or three days. This over-all pattern of results has been obtained in a number of subsequent studies (Heron, et al., 1956; Lilly, 1956). Although subject to a number of interpretations, the general results of these studies strongly suggest that stimulus reduction to this degree was not a pleasurable or reinforcing state of affairs. If anything, stimulus increases were felt to be extremely potent happenings.

Less dramatic, but equally convincing, are a wide variety of experiments which indicate that, under certain conditions, animals will work in order to obtain increases in stimulation. Rats who had been reared in darkness worked at pressing a bar to receive brief durations of light (Roberts et al., 1958). Rhesus monkeys confined in a cage which did not permit a view of the laboratory environment worked persistently on a discrimination problem in which the payoff for a correct response was a brief opportunity to look out of a small window at the "outside world" of the laboratory. This effect did not seem to diminish with repeated trials (Butler, 1953; Butler and Harlow, 1954). In a similar vein, the work of Harlow on manipulatory behavior also suggests that increased stimulation of certain types can be rewarding. Rhesus monkeys were provided with mechanical puzzles, which they worked on for apparently no other reason than the rewards of manipulating the gadgetry (Harlow, et al., 1950).

Although a detailed review of the experimental literature on exploratory, curiosity, and activity needs is unnecessary for the purpose of this section, it should be pointed out that there is an ample supply of well-controlled experiments indicating that increases in stimulation rather than stimulus reductions were the effective motivators of behavior (Berlyne, 1960). Moreover, this body of work rather clearly indicates that the observed increases in activity or exploratory behavior on the part of the organism were not associated with any of the major drive systems, such as seeking of food or water. Here, then, is a line of research which departs from a strict drive- or stimulus-reduction theory of reinforcement.

Another area of experimentation that takes issue with the drive-reduction point of view is that involving taste. P. T. Young (1961), for example, has argued that preferences for certain types of foods (tastes) may be unrelated to any underlying tissue deficits, but reflect the pure affective enjoyment produced by the taste sensations themselves. Experiments in which experimental animals, even when satiated with food and drink, will work to obtain sweet-tasting but nonnutritive saccharin are evidence in support of Young's point of view (Sheffield and Roby, 1950; Sheffield, et al., 1954). That these taste preferences are learned and, thus, could serve as forerunners (conditioned stimuli) of postingestion drive reduction is still a possibility in the interpretation of these data. This issue still awaits experimental clarification.

A third area of research pertinent to the drive- or stimulus-reduction issue is represented by Sheffield, et al. (1951). Here, sexually inexperienced male rats were allowed access to a receptive female after traversing a runway. It was noted that runway speeds increased over trials, even though the sexual activities of the male were consistently interrupted before ejaculation occurred. In this case, since the males had not previously had sexual experiences, there was little possibility that the sexual play had been learned as the prelude to ejaculation. Evidently, the males' behavior was motivated by the opportunities for increased stimulation, rather than by an ultimate reduction in sexual drives.

Taking an overview of the foregoing material, it is evident that a view of motivation based purely on a drive- or stimulus-reduction notion becomes difficult to defend. An increased level of stimulation, an opportunity to explore or manipulate aspects of the environment, or to engage in "pleasurable" activities also seem to be the end points of an organism's behavior under certain circumstances. In total, these types of demonstrations have led to a reconsideration of a new hedonistic view of motivation, i.e., affective states related to enjoyment or aversion can operate as motivators, and these states may be independent of tissue needs. Over the past decade this hedonistic versus drive-reduction issue has become focused most pointedly in studies involving brain stimulation. Thus the following section reviews in some detail the topic of intracranial stimulation.

ELECTRICAL STIMULATION OF THE BRAIN

With respect to theories of motivation, 1954 was a landmark year. At this time Olds and Milner published a paper describing experiments in which laboratory rats learned and maintained a bar-pressing response while the only reinforcement delivered was electrical stimulation to certain areas of the brain. It appeared that this intracranial stimulation (ICS) was "pleasurable" to the animals. The experimental procedure involved a permanently implanted electrode in the brain which was wired in such a way that a brief electrical stimulation occurred when the bar in the Skinner box was pressed by the animal. Naturally, this reinforcement effect was obtained at only certain specific sites in the brain, and the effect has been found to vary depending on the parameters of stimulation (to be discussed in the following). Of primary importance for this discussion, however, was the implication that here was a demonstration of a reward mechanism which presumably was not dependent on drive reduction and, hence, pointed to the possibility of a new, hedonistic theory of motivation.

At about this same time Delgado et al. (1954) demonstrated that electrical stimulation of certain hypothalamic sites in the cat produced aversive effects. The emotional response evoked seemed fearlike, and the stimulation could be used to motivate the learning of behaviors by which to terminate (escape) the stimulation. Of major interest here was the fact that the site of stimulation was not near any of the classical pain pathways. It appeared that a more general circuit of the brain pertaining to the emotional-motivational aspects of aversion, fear, withdrawal, and the like had been tapped.

The findings of both "rewarding" and "aversive" areas of the brain have prompted a decade and a half of subsequent work and controversy surrounding a hedonistic versus drive-reduction view of motivation. Is reinforcement possible without in some way being connected with drive reduction, or are the rewarding effects of brain stimulation still ultimately tied to the tissue demands of the body? As will be seen, the primary focus of this controversy has centered on the reward side of the coin; hence, most of the subsequent material in this chapter will review the work following up that of Olds and Milner.

Some General Aspects of ICS with Humans

Elicitation of the rewarding effects of brain stimulation has been observed in a variety of species. Adding weight to the generality of the phenomenon have been comparable effects with cats, monkeys, dolphins, and humans. The observations with human subjects have typically involved patients with a variety of neurological, physical, or psychiatric disorders in which brain areas have been stimulated for diagnostic or therapeutic reasons. In some cases it has been feasible to implant multilead electrodes (both stimulating and recording), which were kept in place for as long as several months, thus allowing postoperative recovery before stimulation effects were observed.

Delgado and his coworkers (Higgins et al., 1956) cite an interesting case report of an eleven-year-old epileptic boy in whom a small area of abnormality of the temporal lobe was found through this implanted-electrode technique. (Successful surgery eventually produced a complete recovery for the child.) Several interviews were conducted with this child during which specific brain areas were stimulated. Neither the child nor the interviewer knew when these relatively brief stimulations occurred, but careful parallel records of stimulation and verbalizations were kept. It was found that the child was typically emotionally toned down and uncommunicative, speaking only 4 to 17 words per two-minute interval. During periods of electrical stimulation in a particular brain area, his attitude and verbal output changed dramatically. He became animated, optimistic, reported many pleasant feelings, communicated a liking for the interviewer, and his talking increased to an average of 88 words every 2 minutes. Upon the cessation of each stimulation his behavior returned to his previous low level of activity.

Similar reports of stimulation-induced feelings of pleasantness and mood changes in humans have been published by a number of investigators (Delgado and Hamlin, 1956; Sem Jacobsen and Torkildson, 1960; Sem Jacobsen, 1965). Moreover, psychiatric patients have been observed to press a lever quite consistently in order to receive brain stimulation in these pleasurable areas (Bishop et al., 1963). In all, these demonstrations with human subjects provide an interesting and rich body of data pertaining to the neurology of reinforcement and pleasurable feelings. However, the ethical and methodological limitations inherent in the use of human subjects in this area of research have required that the experimentation with animal subjects carry the major burden of elucidating the phenomenon.

Dimensions of the ICS Reinforcement Effect

Most of the experimental work with animal subjects have used the rat; hence considerable anatomical detail is available concerning the pleasure and aversion areas in the brain of this animal. Clear-cut analysis of the comparable human areas is not yet available. These reinforcement areas have been found to be distributed throughout the limbic system (cortical regions at levels below the neocortex, including the olfactory tubercle, hippocampus, septum, cingulate area, and others; see Olds, 1961), the amygdala, hypothalamus, and medial forebrain bundle (a large fiber tract connecting lower cortical centers with the preoptic and lateral areas of the hypothalamus) (Olds, 1960; Olds and Olds, 1963). "Aversive" areas are found far less frequently and are less clearly defined in an anatomical sense (parts of the thalamus, hypothalamus, and tegmentum in the midbrain). A major technical problem encountered by researchers in attempting to map the reinforcement and aversive areas has been the fact that these areas are frequently located in the same vicinity; hence stimulation of one may also produce an effect in the other. This anatomical proximity of areas having opposite effects has led to some complexities in the data that occur when such variables as intensity of stimulation are investigated.

As the intensity of the stimulating current is increased in the posterior hypothalamus of the rat, for example, the self-stimulation rate also increases. This monotonic relationship seems to hold all the way up to the point where stimulation-induced seizures interfere with the animal pressing the bar. As many as 5,000 bar-pressing responses per hour have been obtained at these levels of stimulation (Olds, 1958a). Other sites produce no regular change in self-stimulation rates as current intensity increases, or in rates which first increase and then decrease as a function of stimulation intensity. Furthermore, it has been found that brief stimulation to certain points can be rewarding, whereas stimulation of longer duration becomes aversive (Bower and Miller, 1958). As noted previously, it has been suggested that some of these unusual patterns may be caused by the spread of the stimulating current to adjacent sites which have opposite motivational properties, thus producing a complex interaction between rewarding and aversive effects (Olds, 1961).

One procedural innovation by which to investigate the intensity variable was developed by Stein and Ray (1959). Animals with electrodes implanted in reward areas were, in effect, allowed to set their own stimulation levels. A Skinner box was arranged with two levers wired so that pressing one lever produced a slight decrease in intensity of stimulation, with the other lever providing a slight increase. In this way, each animal could manipulate the intensity of the current to a preferred level. Here, again, it was found that some electrode sites resulted in progressive increases in level of stimulation to the point where motor disturbances affected the bar pressing, whereas at other sites, presumably in the vicinity of aversive brain areas, lower levels of stimulation were maintained.

ICS AND OTHER MOTIVATIONAL SYSTEMS

We now return to the central issue of this chapter: the drive-reduction versus hedonistic view of motivation. On the surface, the results of the ICS studies seem to argue that there are areas or circuits in the brain which subserve the experiences of pleasure and aversion; moreover, stimulation of these areas can serve as a motivator of behavior. A crucial question that has not yet been considered pertains to the overlap between, for example, the "reward" areas of the brain and those sites which subserve other motivational states such as hunger, thirst, and sex. A substantial number of studies suggest that many of the brain areas which are rewarding are also parts of the systems involving these other drives.

Considering the area of hunger first, there have been several demonstrations that, with certain electrode sites, the rate of self-stimulation is related to the degree of food deprivation (e.g., Brady, 1958; Olds, 1958b).

Brady, for example, used 1, 4, 24, or 48 hours of food deprivation for rats and cats, and found that the rate of bar pressing for ICS increased as a function of deprivation level. Similarly, Olds (1958b) alternated access to food with food deprivation on a daily basis and found that, for particular hypothalamic electrode sites, self-stimulation was related to degree of food deprivation. It will be recalled that in Chapter III evidence was presented indicating that electrical stimulation of the lateral hypothalamic area brought about eating behavior. As it turns out, this area also has been found to be one of the more potent sites in the brain for the reinforcing effects of ICS. As a matter of fact, Margules and Olds (1962) found that all sites which produced eating by electrical stimulation also displayed high rates of self-stimulation. Finally, it has been found that stimulation of the ventromedial area of the hypothalamus (a central part of the inhibitory food-satiation mechanism) reduced concurrent self-stimulation to lateral hypothalamic sites (Hoebel and Teitelbaum, 1962).

From this evidence it appears that at least some of the sites which produce reward effects through electrical stimulation are parts of the feeding circuits discussed earlier. Self-stimulation rates at these sites seem to be dependent on level of food deprivation, and there is evidence of some anatomical overlap between the feeding and reward systems. A more elaborate discussion of the implications of these findings will be reserved until some of the other drive systems have been considered.

With respect to the relationship between thirst and ICS, probably the most direct demonstration has been provided by Brady (1958). A water-deprived rat was placed in a two-bar Skinner box. One lever provided a small drink of water each time it was pressed (continuous reinforcement) whereas the other lever resulted in ICS to the septal region. It was found that the rat pressed each bar quite frequently, thereby receiving both water and brain stimulation. After a relatively brief period the bar pressing for water stopped, presumably owing to restoration of the animal's fluid deficit. Of importance was the observation that bar pressing for ICS also stopped at this time, suggesting that the electrical stimulation to this area of the brain was only rewarding while some degree of water deprivation was present. In a second portion of this experiment, the drinks of water were delivered only intermittently following bar pressing, thereby preventing the development of rapid satiation (the ICS was still delivered after every bar press on the other lever). Under these conditions bar pressing for both water and ICS were maintained for a substantially longer period of time. Hence, by prolonging the state of water deprivation, Brady also was able to extend the period of time that septal stimulation was "reinforcing."

The evidence regarding the relationship between ICS and sexual drives appears to be comparable to that for hunger or thirst. Olds (1958*b*), after training animals to respond in a stable fashion for ICS at various electrode sites, castrated the animals, thus producing a declining level of androgen over the next two weeks. Thereafter, administration of testosterone propionate brought about elevated androgen levels followed again by a period of decline. Self-stimulation procedures were carried out throughout these intervals. It was found that, for some electrode sites, there was a positive relationship between androgen level and self-stimulation rate, and for other sites there was a negative correlation (these were some of the sites implicated in feeding behaviors). In a study using female rats, Prescott (1966) noted a positive correlation between self-stimulation rates and estrous-related variations in sexual drive for certain hypothalamic electrode sites. Finally, Miller (1961) reported an interesting anatomical parallel in males that hypothalamic sites producing ejaculation when electrically stimulated also tend to be reward areas for ICS.

RECAPITULATION AND PERSPECTIVE

It is apparent from the evidence just presented that the pleasurable or reward areas in the brain are not completely independent of the circuitry which subserve the major drive systems of the organism. In general, when we consider that such systems as hunger, thirst, and sex have major anatomical foci in the hypothalamic-limbic area, as does the reward system, it is not surprising to find that a high degree of interrelationship exists. This is not to say that all areas that have been found to be rewarding are necessarily directly related to other drive systems. Indeed, there have been studies which indicated that self-stimulation at a certain site was independent of, for example, level of food deprivation (e.g., Reynolds, 1958); however, this kind of negative finding does not rule out the possibility that some other drive system (thirst, sex, temperature) was involved. Naturally this issue cannot be fully resolved until the complex circuitry subserving all the major drive systems has been determined. For the present, then, no clear-cut resolution of the drive-reduction versus hedonism controversy appears possible. Perhaps the real issue is not to conceptualize the problem as an either-or proposition, but to focus on the discovery of the functional and anatomical relationships which exist between the systems.

A closer look at the possible relationship between the ICS reward effect and major drive systems may prove instructive. There is reasonably good evidence that the lateral hypothalamic area is a primary center in the elicitation of feeding behavior (Chapter III). In the normal course of an organism's life, this feeding center is probably triggered by biochemical and thermal stimuli associated with food depletion, thus, in turn, contributing to the elicitation of eating or instrumental behaviors associated with obtaining food. The fact that the lateral hypothalamus has also been found to be a reward area for ICS has led such investigators as Hoebel and Teitelbaum (1962) to suggest that the pleasurable effects of electrical stimulation to the lateral area may be comparable to the gratification achieved by eating.

In the area of sexual behavior, the observation by Miller (1961), that the hypothalamic site which elicited ejaculation in males was also a reward area for ICS, may be viewed in the same way; i.e., the pleasurable effects produced by the artificial electrical stimulation are analogous to the sensations elicited when excitation occurs in this hypothalamic area during normal mating behavior.

Extending this line of thinking, it is possible to view this area of research from a slightly different perspective. Let us return to the basic premise that there are areas and circuits in the brain which subserve pleasurable (and aversive) experiences. Furthermore, it can be argued that various subsystems within these brain areas underlie the varieties and nuances of affective experience, which humans, at least, are so prone to describe. We might ask then, by what multiple means in one's natural life processes is access gained into these pleasurable (and aversive) circuits? At least part of the answer seems to be emerging:

1. The restoration of bodily deficits (eating, drinking) certainly seems to be anatomically related to the pleasure areas.

2. So are the processes associated with reproductive behavior.

3. Quite likely, as suggested by Pfaffman (1961), the classical sensory pathways concerning taste also send collaterals into these affective areas.

4. More speculatively, it is possible that the physiological systems underlying certain varieties of thermal, tactual, and other sensory experience also provide access to these areas. (Comparable processes can be conceptualized for aversive stimulation, and Melzack's work on the sensation of pain, as reviewed in the previous chapter, is consistent with this viewpoint.)

A question that as yet remains unanswered is how learning can affect this phenomenon. At the simplest level it might be asked whether neutral stimuli which have been consistently paired with rewarding ICS can also acquire reinforcing properties (secondary reinforcement). To date, the evidence on this point is contradictory (Stein, 1958; Seward et al., 1959).

SUMMARY

The implications of the work reviewed in this chapter can probably best be discussed in several stages.

First is the question of whether all motivation is ultimately reducible to drive- or stimulus-reduction terms. Here the evidence stemming from research on sexual, exploratory, curiosity, and manipulatory behaviors and sensory deprivation studies argues that a considerable proportion of an organism's activity may be regulated to provide increases in stimulation rather than decreases. Recognition of these classes of behaviors has led Grossman (1967) to demarcate these as *nonhomeostatic* drives in contrast to the more traditional *homeostatic* drives such as hunger and thirst.

In the latter category, Grossman is speaking of drives which are primarily a function of internal stimulation. These stimuli arise typically when some vital biological process deviates from within a relatively narrow range and the organism's responses are organized to restore the physiological process to this "optimum" range. Recall of the material in the chapters on hunger, thirst, and temperature regulations will reveal how complex the processes can be that underlie this homeostatic conceptualization.

According to Grossman's two-factor theory, nonhomeostatic drives are elicited by external stimulation; hence, any discriminable stimulus is potentially capable of evoking a drive. However, attributing motivational properties to the sensory input alone would be an oversimplification. The theory points out that the biological state of the organism interacts with the external stimulation in the elicitation of drive-related behaviors. Thus, for example, the level of circulating estrogen in the female rat plays a major role in determining her approach and copulatory behaviors in the presence of a male. Similarly, whether or not manipulatory or curiosity behaviors will be elicited in a monkey at the sight of an intriguing puzzle may depend on reduced levels of such drives as hunger and thirst. In a sense, then, the manifestation of these nonhomeostatic drives depends on a complex interaction of the external and internal environments of the organism, with the behavior of an organism at any moment in time being the resultant of competition among a variety of motivational systems.

Both homeostatic and nonhomeostatic drives appear to be closely related to the ICS reinforcement phenomenon. There is evidence that the neurological and biochemical processes which underlie such homeostatic drives as hunger and thirst are intimately related to the reward areas of the brain. By implication it appears that those sites in the brain associated with consummatory responses are also sites that are found to be rewarding when electrically stimulated. Conversely, there is suggestive evidence that brain areas responsive to bodily depletion may also be areas producing aversive effects. Although these generalizations are assuredly oversimplifications, they may well represent first approximations to a conceptualization of some of the reward-aversive areas in the central nervous system.

The relationship between nonhomeostatic drives and ICS can be represented by the research on sexual behavior, where brain areas associated with sexual arousal and copulatory behavior seem to elicit rewarding effects when electrically stimulated. Perhaps, again, the physiological processes temporarily elicited by ICS to these sites are comparable to the processes which take place during normal sexual behaviors.

From an evolutionary point of view we might argue that those very biological processes concerning survival of the organism or propagation of the species overlap (or are the same as) those physiological systems which subserve the affective experiences of pleasantness or aversion. Species which did not have these overlapping systems probably are long extinct.

IX

Future Perspectives

When we stop to consider the material in the preceding chapters, we inevitably come to the conclusion that living organisms are marvelous things. The ability to make very sensitive physiological and behavioral adjustments to changes in the environment, the finely programmed sequencing of neural and biochemical events in coordinating behavior, the vast ability to store information and use it in appropriate situations, all provoke a philosophical reaction to the genius of nature. Equally provoking is the knowledge that there is so much still to be learned.

The foregoing material is, of course, merely a small segment in the study of behavior, albeit a very basic aspect of life. These so-called *survival* functions in many ways form the building blocks upon which more complex interpersonal behaviors are constructed. The very interesting study of social motivations is a natural outgrowth of the current topics. Equally fascinating, however, are the as yet unanswered questions which remain in the physiological-motivation area. Most of these have already been touched upon in earlier chapters, and the current sections are designed merely to summarize these future perspectives. Perhaps some of the readers of this book will become the researchers who unravel these basic questions. The following, then, reviews briefly some of the major issues which will probably command attention over the next several decades.

THE TRANSMISSION OF NEURAL INFORMATION

It is commonplace to state that we all at times appreciate the richness of sensory experiences. Viewing a beautiful landscape or listening to a great symphony provides a subtlety of detail which is remarkable. Even more remarkable, however, is a consideration of the problem of how complex stimuli in the visual, auditory, or other sense modalities are communicated to the brain. After the stimuli are detected by the sense organ (e.g., the retina of the eye), they are translated into neural events which project, via the sensory nerve fibers, to the brain. In terms of the basic events that occur in these sensory systems, there are only a limited number of parameters. These are: the neural systems which are innervated; the number of activated neural units; and the temporal pattern of nerve firing (frequency of nerve impulses). In some way, then, the physical stimuli from the environment are encoded in the sensory system using the aforementioned parameters, ultimately to provide the conscious experience of the event. Breaking this code seems to be one of the major electrophysiological problems still to be solved. It will be recalled that this issue came up with respect to the topics of taste (Chapter III), thermal stimulation (Chapter V), and pain (Chapter VII). For a recent treatment of this topic, the reader is referred to Uttal and Krishoff (1967).

CORTICAL EFFECTS ON SENSORY INPUT

There is an added problem in attempting to understand the code of the sensory systems. This is the fact that the higher central-nervous-system structures apparently can modulate the electrical activity in the incoming sensory channel. Recall in Chapter II the demonstration by Hernandez-Peon that the electrical activity in the peripheral auditory system of the cat produced by a sound stimulus was inhibited when the cat's attention was drawn to a mouse. Similarly, Melzack's theory of pain (Chapter VII) took into account that neural activity in pain fibers could be affected by higher centers in the nervous system. In fact, it appears that most of the sensory systems in the body are not purely sensory; i.e., there are also efferent fibers involved which regulate the input into the brain. All this points in the direction of what might be termed *selective perception.* It appears that organisms do not just automatically take in and record all sensory stimuli, but that some sort of neural gating and filtering take place. What the nature of this selection process is, what neural structures are involved, and what variables affect this process is a wide-open area for investigation.

MEMORY STORAGE

There is an old adage which states that past experiences are indelibly marked in the brain and are never really lost. Recent advances in brain stimulation studies suggest that this notion may have some basis in fact. Penfield and his associates (1954) have been able to stimulate electrically various portions of the cortex in human subjects while undergoing brain surgery. These procedures frequently elicited highly detailed and vivid recollections of specific events, to the degree that the subject felt he was actually reliving the previous experience. Comparable findings have been obtained by subsequent investigators using chronically implanted electrodes in humans. These observations have lead to a resurgence of interest in discovering the physiological sites and processes involved in information storage.

Related to this is the ever-present issue concerning the physiological site of learning. When one learns, is this mediated by a change in neural connections or some subtle biochemical alteration in neural cells, or both? To date no one really knows. There has, however, been some suggestive work involving ribonucleic acid (RNA), which is one of the biochemical substances implicated in genetic transmission. In the area of memory and learning, the transfer of RNA into conducting neurons and subsequent changes in the protein structure of the neuron have been suggested as one of the basic mechanisms involved (Landauer, 1964). Here, then, is another whole area of investigation opening up which may lead to an understanding of one of the most fundamental processes in living organisms.

PHYSIOLOGICAL MECHANISMS OF REINFORCEMENT

Another viewpoint on the physiology of learning is the question of how reinforcement operates at a physical level. Throughout this book there have been numerous references to the physiological processes involved in reinforcement, and we have seen the beginnings of a systematic study of positive emotions in Chapter VIII. It is apparent that the relationship between reinforcement and other motivational systems is basic, and subsequent work will probably continue to elucidate the overlap between these various biological systems and their relationship to overt behavior.

THE PROGRAMMING OF COMPLEX BEHAVIORS

Did you ever hear a pianist play Chopin's Minute Waltz? It is always amazing how an individual can have such control over his fingers. Moreover, it illustrates one of the other basic questions about behavior. What physiological processes program and store this type of highly complex motor responding? We know, of course, that the area in front of the central sulcus in the cortex and also the cerebellum are major motor centers in the brain, but it is just a matter of speculation as to how movements are organized in these areas. This issue came up in another form in Chapter

III. Here, it will be recalled, several experiments were cited in which stimulation of the lateral hypothalamus evoked completely organized, previously learned food-seeking responses. In some way, then, the organism must be able to store and "call up" preprogrammed sequences of responding, which, by the way, are also flexible enough to adapt to at least minor alterations in the setting in which the behavior is to be carried out.

SOCIAL-PHYSIOLOGICAL RELATIONSHIPS

The discussion of complex behaviors inevitably leads us to a consideration of social processes. Indeed, social behavior has been touched on in our discussions of sex and aversive stimulation, but obviously the whole realm of emotions and their relationship to interpersonal behavior has been omitted. Perhaps the work of Delgado in recent years has done most to stimulate interest in the neurology of interpersonal behavior and, particularly, the physiological concomitants of emotional responses. With his developments of multiple electrode implants, permanently implanted cannullas, and remote-control procedures in a whole colony of primates, we appear to be on the threshold of some major insights into the mechanisms involved in both aggression and friendly behaviors. Considering the vast political and cultural problems we face in today's world, these insights will come none too soon.

Appendix

An Orientation to the Nervous System

This is not a book on physiology; however, to understand the physical process involved in motivation, it will be necessary for the student to have an overview of the bodily systems involved. This appendix is intended to provide a superficial review of the anatomy of the central and autonomic nervous systems and some related endocrine (hormonal) functions. Emphasis will be placed on those structures that are primarily related to motivational phenomena.

THE CENTRAL NERVOUS SYSTEM

This is the vastly complex bioelectric system of the body. It functions generally in a dual fashion: (*a*) to transmit information about the environment and the body to the brain where it is recorded, stored, and compared with other information and (*b*) to carry information back to the muscles and other action (effector) systems of the body, thus in a sense, programming behavior. In the study of motivation, then, it is of primary importance to be able to specify (*a*) the nature of the information transmission with respect to such things as painful stimulation, sexual drives, or water and food deficits; (*b*) what structures in the system record this information; and (*c*) how the system triggers responses which attempt to restore the body's equilibrium.

The central nervous system is generally viewed as having two main divisions: the spinal cord and the brain. The former is encased in a bony structure called the *spinal column* and runs the length of the trunk, and the latter, of course, is contained within the skull. There are several ways in which the brain can be subdivided, but for this discussion it seems most reasonable simply to highlight some of the more important structures and systems. Starting from the lowest part of the brain (where it connects with the upper part of the spinal cord), the following areas will be reviewed: the medulla; the cerebellum and pons; the midbrain; the diencephalon; and the cerebrum. To help the reader, the following conventional terminology is used to indicate directions in the brain: assuming an organism on all fours, *anterior* refers to areas toward the front of the

147

head, *posterior* or *caudal* being in the tail direction. Areas toward the top of the head are termed *dorsal,* and *ventral* refers to areas at the base. Viewing the nervous system as having a midline, structures close to the midline are termed *medial* and those more distant are designated as *lateral.*

The Spinal Cord

The primary characteristic of the spinal cord is that of a great conduction pathway connecting the brain with almost all parts of the body (the exception is the head, where separate cranial nerves serve this function). Thus stimulation of the trunk, limbs, or the internal structures is translated into electric impulses in the peripheral nerves. These enter the spinal cord and eventuate in electrical activity in one or several of the large *afferent* fiber tracts projecting upwards to the brain. Likewise, neural activity arising in the brain is transmitted downward through the *efferent* fiber tracts in the cord which control the major response systems of the body. Thus the large bulk of sensory information from the body *and* the major part of the motor impulses regulating behavior pass through the spinal cord. It is little wonder that damage to this conduction pathway can have such profound effects as paralysis and/or loss of sensation from the body.

A somewhat closer look at a cross section of the spinal cord would be instructive. The schematic of the cord in Figure A.1 shows the main aspects of the structure, with the interior gray matter consisting of short fibers and cell bodies approximately in a butterfly shape, and the large upward- and downward-coursing fiber tracts (white matter) situated to the outside.

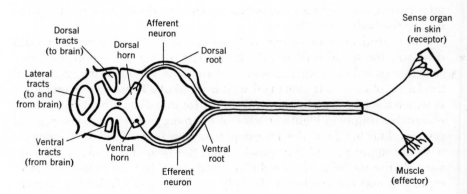

Figure A.1 Cross section of the spinal cord, also showing a schematic of the sensory input from receptors and motor outflow to the muscles.

In the figure it can be seen that the *ventral horn* (gray matter) contains cells the axons of which are motor in function; i.e., ventral root fibers eventuate in muscle which control movement and postural activity. The dorsal horn cells receive incoming (afferent) impulses from the dorsal root fibers, transmitting them to the brain and other levels of the cord. These latter, intracord connections are effected by relatively short *intersegmental* tracts to motor cells and support a variety of reflexes at the spinal level. Impulses transmitted to the brain eventuate in the medulla, cerebellum, pons, midbrain, and thalamus.

The upward- and downward-coursing fiber tracts (fasciculi) of the white matter are demarcated into three columns: the dorsal, lateral, and ventral. These columns (*funiculi*) are each made up of nerve fiber tracts which subserve sensory-motor functions. Table A.1 outlines some of the major tracts and their functions.

The Brain

As indicated earlier, the brain can be conveniently subdivided into several parts: the medulla, cerebellum, pons, midbrain, diencephalon, and

Table A.1   Major Tracts of the Spinal Cord

Column	To Brain (Afferent)	From Brain (Efferent)
Lateral	1. Spinocerebellar tracts—impulses to the cerebellum concerned with coordinated voluntary movement. 2. Lateral spinothalamic tracts—impulses concerning pain, and thermal stimuli.	1. Lateral corticospinal tracts—impulses from cortex to ventral horn cells. 2. Rubrospinal tracts—impulses concerned with coordination and muscle tonus. 3. Tectospinal tracts—impulses affecting visual-motor coordination.
Ventral	1. Ventral spinothalamic tracts—impulses to thalamus concerning touch and pressure.	1. Ventral corticospinal tracts—impulses from cortex to ventral horn cells. 2. Vestibulospinal tracts—impulses from medulla to ventral horn cells, concerned with equilibrium.
Posterior	1. Fasciculus gracilis 2. Fasciculus cuneatus—impulses to medulla (relayed to thalamus and cortex) concerning touch and muscular movement.	

the cerebrum. The medulla, pons, and midbrain (the brain stem) appear as a relatively slender stalk on which the overshadowing cerebrum is situated. The cerebellum is located in a cavity behind the medulla and pons. Figure A.2 may serve as a reference in generally locating these structures.

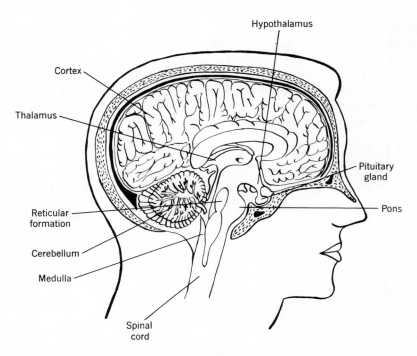

Figure A.2   The major structures of the human brain.

Medulla. This structure is located at the base of the cranial cavity and is continuous with the upper end of the spinal cord. It is distinct from the cord in that new substructures are included and a rearrangement of cord processes is apparent. Sensory and motor nuclei related to cranial nerves and *autonomic nuclei* concerned with such vital functions as respiration, heart rate, and blood pressure are found in the medulla.

At this level the ventral and lateral corticospinal tracts merge into one large tract. This is accomplished by a crossing over (decussation) of the lateral corticospinal tract from one side of the medulla to the other. In addition, the fasciculi gracile and cuneatus terminate in nuclei where connections (synapses) are made with fibers which project upward as *internal arcuate* fibers. These fibers also decussate and proceed to the thalamus in a tract called the *medial lemniscus*.

Pons. The ventral portion of the pons contains several features of interest. Corticospinal fibers (projecting downward from the cortex) pass through and corticopontile fibers make synaptic connections (along with collateral corticospinal fibers) in the *nuclei pontis*. These nuclei, in turn, have fibers which (via the middle cerebellar peduncle) enter the cerebellum (along with the ventral spinocerebellar tract).

The dorsal area of the pons contains the terminations of the cochlear nerve (from the ear) in the *cochlear nuclei*. Fibers from these nuclei proceed in several directions—to the reticular formation (see the following) and to the tract of the lateral lemniscus. Also in this area are nuclei of the vestibular nerve and several other of the cranial nerves.

Reticular Formation. The space between the pons and medulla consists of a relatively ill-defined mass of white and gray matter containing numerous nuclei and is commonly termed the *brain stem reticular formation* (BSRF). Many fiber systems form interconnections between various parts of the reticular formation and there are afferent fibers incoming from the major sensory pathways and from a variety of other brain areas. Reticular activity has been correlated with EEG records of cortical processes, behavioral signs of alertness, and portions of this area have been found to be sensitive to epinephrine, thus implicating it as an important structure in the study of sleep, arousal and attention.

Cerebellum. This structure lies behind the medulla and pons and consists of a central *vermis* and two larger masses known as the *cerebellar hemispheres*. The structure is composed of white matter with a cortex (covering) of gray matter and has the appearance of bundles of tightly packed leaves. Connections with the rest of the central nervous system are via three pairs of fiber tracts—the *inferior, middle,* and *superior cerebellar peduncles.* Incoming fibers from the spinocerebellar tracts and from the vestibular nuclei of the medulla are via the inferior peduncle. Fibers from the nuclei pontis (in the pons) transmit impulses arising in the cerebral cortex through the middle peduncle. The superior peduncle is composed of both efferent and afferent tracts, the efferents, arising in cerebellar nuclei, proceeding both to the thalamus (with impulses relayed to the motor area of the cerebral cortex) and downward through the spinal cord to the ventral horn cells of the cord. Afferent fibers transmit kinesthetic impulses from sensory cells in the muscles and joints via the spinocerebellar tracts.

The function of the cerebellum is to coordinate and smooth out skeletal movements. This is accomplished via its connections with the motor area of the cerebral cortex and with the motor cells in the spinal cord. The afferent, kinesthetic feedback received from muscles also provides a mechanism for precise and regulated voluntary motor behaviors. Finally, afferent impulses from the vestibular apparatus in the ear permit postural adjustments for the body's equilibrium.

Midbrain. This area constitutes the top of the brain stalk and is composed of several structures. A ventral view exhibits two columns—the *cerebral peduncles*—which are separated by the *cerebral aqueduct* from two pairs of small hemispheres called the *superior* and *inferior colliculi.* These latter structures are involved in reflex movements caused by visual or auditory stimulation. The midbrain also contains nuclei with reciprocal connections to the cerebellum and cerebral cortex as well as nuclei for several of the cranial nerves (III and IV). Included in this area also is the *red nucleus,* an oval mass of cells on each side of the roof of the midbrain. Incoming fibers are from the cerebellum over the superior peduncle, the corpus striatum, and the cerebral cortex and are relayed to the ventral horn cells of the spinal cord.

Diencephalon. This area is composed of the *hypothalamus,* the *medial* and *lateral geniculate bodies,* and the *thalamus.*

Any book on the physiological basis of motivation would have to devote most of its discussion to the hypothalamus. By far it is the single most important center in the brain with respect to the elicitation and coordination of motivated behaviors, and, as such, has been a focal point of discussion in most chapters in this book. This section attempts merely to introduce the student to this structure, with more detailed treatment having been provided in the remainder of the book.

The hypothalamus is a relatively small structure located close to the base of the brain. In spite of its small size, its wide-reaching effects seem to be caused by at least five different characteristics: (*a*) it has many well-defined nuclei which have rather specific functions; (*b*) it is in complex interactions with other nervous system structures (the limbic areas particularly); (*c*) it exerts a direct, coordinating effect on the autonomic nervous system; (*d*) it strongly influences the adjacent pituitary gland (the so-called *master gland* of the body) which, in turn, controls many other hormonal structures of the body; and (*e*) it is an area richly endowed with blood vessels. It has been found that various portions of the hypothalamus are sensitive to changes in the chemistry of the blood; thus it is a site of neural-biochemical coordination as well.

Figure A.3 is an oversimplified schematic of some of the nuclei of the

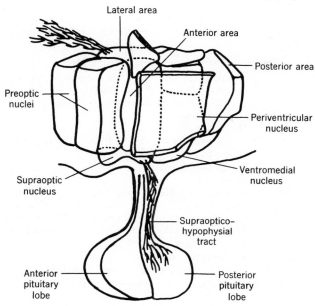

Lateral area

Anterior area

Posterior area

Preoptic nuclei

Periventricular nucleus

Ventromedial nucleus

Supraoptic nucleus

Supraoptico–hypophysial tract

Anterior pituitary lobe

Posterior pituitary lobe

Figure A.3 Some of the major nuclei of the hypothalamus along with the connections to the pituitary gland.

hypothalamus, along with the connections to the pituitary. A brief summary of the relationships between these nuclei and other response systems is presented in Table A.2. As can be seen, the hypothalamus is involved in the major "survival" functions of the organism.

One of the most interesting areas of interaction between the nervous and chemical systems in the body is that which takes place between the hypothalamus and the pituitary gland. This latter structure, located at the base of the brain, controls many other hormonal secretions through its own hormonal output. These *trophic* hormones from the pituitary circulate in the bloodstream and exert chemical control over the target glands, causing these distant endocrines to secrete other hormones. In this fashion, ultimate control over a vast array of biochemical substances is invested in the hypothalamus.

The pituitary consists of two lobes—the anterior and posterior. Only the latter has direct neural connections with the hypothalamus. Hypothalamic control over the anterior lobe seems to be a two-stage affair. Nerve impulses release chemical substances into the median eminence, which are then transported via a vascular portal system to the anterior area. These chemical transmitters then appear to produce the secretion of the

Table A.2

Hypothalamic Area	Systems Influenced
1. Posterior	Sympathetic division of the autonomic nervous system. Secretion of adrenalin from adrenal cortex. Heat maintenance in cold environments. General arousal. Wake center.
2. Anterior	Parasympathetic division of the autonomic nervous system. Heat loss in hot environments. Sexual behavior. Sleep center.
3. Lateral	Eating and drinking behavior. Area of positive reinforcement for electrical stimulation.
4. Ventromedial	Inhibitory area for eating and possibly drinking.
5. Supraoptic	Secretion of antidiuretic hormone. Important in maintaining water balance.
6. Preoptic	Thermal regulation. Indirect effects on eating and drinking.

anterior hormones. The trophic hormones from the anterior lobe have direct effects on hormonal secretions in the gonads and, thus, have great influence on sexual behavior and reproduction. In addition, a trophic hormone (thyrotrophin) regulates activity in the thyroid gland and thereby influences general metabolism and growth. Finally, an anterior trophic hormone called *adrenotrophin* (ACTH) stimulates the adrenal cortex in its output of steroids. These have a variety of functions ranging from influencing metabolism rate to maintaining electrolyte balance in the chemistry of the body.

The primary trophic hormones secreted from the posterior lobe of the pituitary are antidiuretic hormone (produced in neurosecretory cells in the hypothalamus) and oxytocin. The former is concerned with the maintenance of water balance and the latter with some aspects of nursing behavior.

Continuing with the description of the diencephalon, the *geniculate bodies* are small, oval structures below each side of the posterior thalamus. The medial geniculate body transmits afferent auditory impulses to the temporal lobe of the cerebral cortex and is also connected with the inferior colliculus, mediating reflexes concerned with auditory stimulation. The lateral geniculates transmit impulses in the visual system to the occipital lobe of the cerebral cortex. Connections are also made with the superior colliculus, again involving visual reflexes.

The thalamus consists of a pair of large masses of gray matter, embedded deep in each cerebral hemisphere. It is composed of many nuclei which are essentially relays for afferent inputs from the major sensory systems (heat, cold, touch, pressure, kinesthetic) to the cerebral cortex. Ascending impulses from the spinal cord, brain stem, and cerebellum enter this region, with some, such as pain fibers, terminating in the thalamus.

Cerebrum. This area is the large umbrellalike dome of the brain, and in humans constitutes about half of the weight of the entire central nervous system. The cerebrum is divided by a longitudinal cleft into two *cerebral hemispheres.* The surface of each hemisphere has many convolutions and wrinkles, the elevations being termed *gyri,* and the depressions called *sulci* (or fissures, if large). The outer bark of the cerebrum is composed of gray matter and is designated as the *cerebral cortex,* whereas the underlying white matter is arranged in a radiating fan shape and is composed of ascending and descending fiber tracts. The central sulcus and the lateral fissure (see Figure A.4) to a large degree divide the cerebral hemispheres into several areas: the *frontal, temporal, parietal,* and *occipital lobes.*

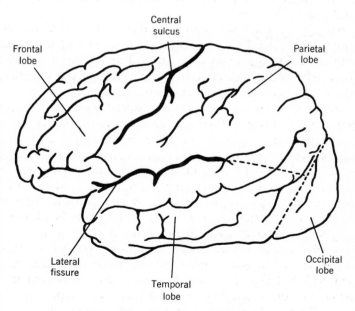

Figure A.4   Lobes of the cortex.

Nerve fibers in the cerebral cortex can be generally divided into three categories: (*a*) *projection* fibers connecting the cortex with other parts of the brain; (*b*) *association* fibers connecting different parts of the cortex; and (*c*) *commissural* fibers which cross from one hemisphere to the other at the base of the longitudinal fissure (the corpus callosum).

Projection fibers extending below the cerebral cortex collect in a relatively narrow column, and this bundle of both ascending and descending fibers is called the *internal capsule.* Descending fibers involved in motor functions eventuate in the pons, cerebellum, and ventral horn cells of the spinal cord, whereas ascending fibers transmit impulses from the thalamus for all the sensory modalities to the various sensory areas of the cortex.

The area in the frontal cortex, immediately in front of the central sulcus, contains cells (pyramidals) governing voluntary motor behavior; hence this region is termed the *motor cortex.* The arrangement of these cells is interesting in that separate groups of the cells appear to control distinct muscles in the body, and the entire musculature has "representation" in this area. In addition, the muscles on one side of the body are almost completely controlled by the motor cortex of the opposite hemisphere (recall the decussation of the corticospinal tracts). The region in front of the motor cortex, called the *premotor area,* also is involved in motor behavior, presumably influencing the coordination of muscular acts into purposeful movements.

Yet further forward in the frontal lobes there is little evidence of direct motor effects. Considerable ambiguity exists concerning the exact functions of this area. As a general rule, surgical lesions produce little gross intellectual deficit, although clinical reports indicate the possibility that alterations in character traits or emotionality may occur.

The cortical areas behind the central sulcus have been termed the *somesthetic cortex,* because they appear to be the terminal site for impulses concerning the sense of touch, pressure, warm, cold, taste, and kinesthetic afferents from the musculature. Again, this region appears to maintain a topographical representation of the body, with, for example, impulses from the lower limb entering the upper area of the sulcus and those from the face entering the lower part of the sulcus. Interestingly, the more important tactual areas of the body (e.g., the hands) have proportionally larger areas of somesthetic cortex devoted to them.

Parts of the temporal lobe have an auditory sensory function, and portions also receive impulses from the vestibular apparatus in the ear concerned with balance. This lobe has been also implicated in several motivational functions, notably sexual drives and hunger. In addition, deep within the lobe is a sensory area concerned with olfaction. Lastly, this lobe apparently plays a role in memory and the storage of prior experience.

The occipital lobe is primarily a visual sensory and association area, being the terminus of fiber systems in the visual system.

The Visceral Brain. This brain region, subserving many aspects of emotional and motivated behavior, has been termed the *visceral brain* or *limbic system.* It consists of the *hippocampus* and the *cingulate gyrus,* parts of the *frontal* and *temporal cortex,* several *thalamic* and *hypothalamic* nuclei, parts of the *basal ganglia,* and the *amygdaloid bodies.*

Certain thalamic nuclei appear to be involved in reflex facial movements during emotional states. The hypothalamus is intimately concerned with such motivational processes as hunger, thirst, sex, and temperature regulation. In addition, the organization of rage responses has been attributed to this region as well as control over the autonomic nervous system (see the following) and a wide variety of hormonal effects.

Lesions in the temporal lobes frequently result in altered or disturbed emotional behaviors. Clinically, in man, these symptoms have ranged from hallucinations, defective reality testing, and dreamlike states of consciousness to psychomotor epilepsy and uncontrolled motor behaviors. They are also apparently involved in sexual motivation in that removal of the temporal lobes frequently results in increased sexual activity. The amygdala and hippocampus also are involved in sexual behavior and reproduction, with certain cells in hippocampus being sensitive to gonadal hormones.

Many groups of cells in the limbic system seem to subserve the subjective experiences of pleasure and pain, in that electrical stimulation of these sites produces stable rates of self-stimulation (pleasurable) or avoidance behaviors in pain areas.

THE AUTONOMIC NERVOUS SYSTEM

Nervous control of the heart muscle and the smooth muscles of the viscera and glands is accomplished by the autonomic nervous system. In this fashion heart-muscle activity, constriction or dilation of blood vessels in the body or bronchioles in the lungs, secretion of hormones from the adrenal medulla and other glands, activity in the gastrointestinal tract, and processes in the reproductive organs are all affected by this system. It is, then, a system that has widespread and critical functions in terms of organizing visceral processes in support of basic life processes and in meeting environmental demands on the organism.

Neural control of the system occurs at several levels: portions of the basal and medial cerebrum are involved via descending fibers to the hypothalamus and brain stem; efferents from nuclei in the hypothalamus (posterior and anterior areas) descend to visceral nuclei in the brain stem; and from these visceral centers projections occur to the nuclei of several cranial nerves and to fibers in the spinal cord (the lateral and anterior columns).

The autonomic nervous system is typically categorized into the *sympathetic* and *parasympathetic* divisions. The former can also be labeled as *thoracolumbar*, since these are the regions of the spinal cord (middle and lower middle) where sympathetic fibers emerge. The parasympathetic division has fibers emanating from both the cranial and sacral (lower) regions and, hence, can be designated as *craniosacral*.

Sympathetic Division

Sympathetic fibers exit the cord (along with other motor neurons) in the ventral nerve roots and then exit this nerve trunk in a conduit called the *white ramus*, eventuating in a group of cells termed a *sympathetic* or *collateral ganglion*. Each side of the spinal column has a chain (21 to 23) of these ganglia which form interconnected cords. The *preganglionic fibers* have a whitish covering (myelin sheath) and are called *white rami communicantes*. Some unmyelinated axons leave the sympathetic ganglia (postganglionic fibers) via the *gray rami communicantes* and rejoin peripheral nerve trunks from which they eventuate in target structures, such as blood vessels, sweat glands, and smooth muscles in the skin. Others proceed directly to organs and blood vessels in the head, neck, thorax, abdomen, and pelvis.

Parasympathetic Division

Preganglionic fibers in this craniosacral division typically extend for considerable distances and enter ganglia near or in the target tissue. Hence postganglionic fibers are typically short. In contrast to the sympathetic division, the ganglia are not interconnected to any extent; thus parasympathetic effects tend to be more specific than the more mass-acting sympathetic processes.

Interaction

As a rule, target structures are innervated by both sympathetic and parasympathetic fibers, and the effects of each are antagonistic. Autonomic processes, therefore, reflect various degrees of balance between these systems, depending on the demands placed on the organism at any particular time. As a general rule, sympathetic effects are energy mobilizing and support vigorous activity, whereas parasympathetic processes are concomitants of bodily restoration. For example, stimulation of sympathetic cardiac accelerator nerves produces increases in heart rate and blood pressure, whereas stimulation of parasympathetic nerves (vagus) produces a slowing down of the heart. Certainly the interaction is more complex than this, and some of the major effects of each system are summarized in Table A.3 and Figure A.5.

Table A.3

Organ	Parasympathetic	Sympathetic
Eye, iris	Constriction.	Dilitation.
Lungs	Secretion of mucous and constriction of bronchioles.	Dilatation of bronchioles.
Heart	Inhibition—heart rate decrease.	Acceleration of heart rate.
Gastrointestinal	Enhances digestion, peristalsis, and evacuation.	Inhibition of peristalsis.
Adrenal medulla		Secretion of epinephrine.
Peripheral blood vessels		Constriction.
Sweat glands and cutaneous smooth muscle		Increase sweating and pilo-erection.

Chemical Transmitters

Transmission of impulses at the synapses in sympathetic and parasympathetic ganglia is mediated by a chemical substance called *acetylcholine*. This *cholinergic* effect also takes place at the termination of parasympathetic postganglionic fibers (in the target tissue), and it is this transmitter substance that acts upon the target cells. Acetylcholine is also released in most of the postganglionic sympathetic terminations in the smooth muscle and sweat glands of the skin. Another transmitter substance, *norepinephrine*, is released at other postganglionic sympathetic terminations, and it is this *adrenergic* substance that affects the target tissue in a druglike fashion. Incidentally, epinephrine (also an adrenergic substance) is released from the adrenal medulla under sympathetic stimulation; this substance, circulating through the blood stream, can thereby enhance sympathetic effects at other sites.

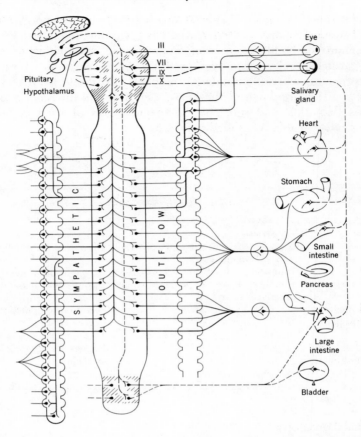

Figure A.5 Schematic of the autonomic nervous system. Sympathetic projections are shown as solid lines and parasympathetic fibers have broken lines. Autonomic projections to the head and organs of the trunk are shown on the right side of the figure. Fibers on the left side represent sympathetic outflow to blood vessels, sweat glands, and smooth muscles associated with hair cells of the skin. (Adapted with permission from E. Gardner, *Fundamentals of Neurology*, 5th ed. Philadelphia: W. B. Saunders, 1963, pp. 232.)

References

Ademetz, J. H. Rate of recovery of functioning in cats with rostral reticular lesions. *Journal of Neurosurgery,* 1959, **16,** 85–97.

Adey, W. R., J. P. Segundo, & R. B. Livingston. Corticifugal influences on intrinsic brainstem conduction in cat and monkey. *Journal of Neurophysiology,* 1957, **20,** 1.

Adolph, E. F. The regulation of the water content of the human organism. *Journal of Physiology* (London), 1921, **55,** 114–132.

Adolph, E. F. Measurements of water drinking in dogs. *American Journal of Physiology,* 1939, **125,** 75–86.

Adolph, E. F. *Physiological Regulations.* Jacques Catell Press, Lancaster, Pa., 1943.

Adolph, E. F. Urges to eat and drink in rats. *American Journal of Physiology,* 1947, **151,** 110–125.

Adolph, E. F. Thirst and its inhibition in the stomach. *American Journal of Physiology,* 1950, **161,** 374–386.

Adrian, E. D. The all-or-none principle in nerve. *Journal of Physiology* (London), 1914, **47,** 460–474.

Allen, W. F. Origin and distribution of the tractus solitarius in the guinea pig. *Journal of Comparative Neurology,* 1923, **35,** 171–204.

Altman, J. & G. D. Das. Autoradiographic and histological evidence of postnatal hippocampal neurogenesis in rats. *Journal of Comparative Neurology,* 1965, **124,** 319–336.

Amsel, A. The role of frustrative nonreward in noncontinuous reward situations. *Psychological Bulletin,* 1958, **55,** 102–119.

Amsel, A., & J. S. Ward. Motivational properties of frustration: II. Frustration drive stimulus and frustration reduction in selective learning. *Journal of Experimental Psychology,* 1954, **48,** 37–47.

Anand, B. K. Nervous regulation of food intake. *Physiological Review,* 1961, **41,** 677–708.

Anand, B. K. & J. R. Brobeck. Hypothalamic control of food intake. *Yale Journal of Biology and Medicine,* 1951, **24,** 123–140.

Anand, B. K., S. Dua & B. Singh. Electrical activity of the hypothalamic feeding centers under the effect of changes in blood chemistry. *Electroencephalography and Clinical Neurophysiology,* 1961, **13,** 54–59.

Anand, B. K., G. S. Chhina, K. N. Sharma, S. Dua & B. Singh. Activity of single neurons in the hypothalamic feeding centers: effect of glucose. *American Journal of Physiology,* 1964, **207,** 1146–1154.

Andersson, B. The effect of injections of hypertonic NaCl solutions into different parts of the hypothalamus of goats. *Acta Physiologica Scandinavica,* 1953, **28,** 188–201.

Andersson, B. & S. M. McCann. A further study of polydipsia evoked by hypothalamic stimulation in the goat. *Acta Physiologica Scandinavica,* 1955, **33,** 333–346.

161

Andersson, B., R. Grant & B. Larsson. Central control of heat loss mechanisms in the goat. *Acta Physiologica Scandinavica,* 1956, **37,** 261–280.

Andersson, B. & B. Larsson. Influence of local temperature changes in the preoptic area and rostral hypothalamus on the regulation of food and water intake. *Acta Physiologica Scandinavica,* 1961, **52,** 75–89.

Andersson, B., C. Gale & J. Sundsten. Preoptic influences on water intake. In M. J. Wayner (Ed.), *Thirst: First International Symposium on Thirst in the Regulation of Body Water.* Oxford: Pergamon Press, 1964, pp. 361–379.

Annau, Z. & L. J. Kamin. The conditioned emotional response as a function of intensity of the US. *Journal of Physiological and Comparative Psychology,* 1961, **54,** 428–432.

Armstrong, R. H., D. Burnap, A. Jacobson, A. Kales, S. Ward & J. Golden. Gastric secretions during sleep and dreaming. Washington, D.C.: APSS, 1965.

Aserinsky, E. & N. Kleitman. Regularly occurring periods of eye motility and concomitant phenomena during sleep. *Science,* 1953, **118,** 273–274.

Aulsebrook, K. A. Effect of vasopression on sodium transfer by rat colon *in vitro. Endocrinology,* 1961, **68,** 1063–1065.

Ax, A. F. The physiological differentiation between fear and anger in humans. *Psychosomatic Medicine,* 1953, **15,** 433–442.

Azrin, N. H. Effects of punishment intensity during variable-interval reinforcement. *Journal of Experimental Analysis of Behavior,* 1960, 3, 123–142.

Bandura, A. Punishment revisited. *Journal of Consulting Psychology,* 1962, **26,** 298–301.

Basowitz, H., H. Persky, S. J. Korchin & R. R. Grinker. *Anxiety and Stress.* New York: McGraw-Hill, 1955.

Bates, M. W., S. F. Nauss, N. C. Hagman & J. Mayer. Fat metabolism in three forms of experimental obesity: body composition. *American Journal of Physiology,* 1955, **180,** 301–309.

Beach, F. A. Effects of cortical lesions upon the copulatory behavior of male rats. *Journal of Comparative Psychology,* 1940, **29,** 193–245.

Beach, F. A. Analysis of the stimuli adequate to elicit mating behavior in the sexually inexperienced male rat. *Journal of Comparative Psychology,* 1942, **33,** 163–207.

Beach, F. A. A review of physiological and psychological studies of sexual behavior in mammals. *Physiological Review,* 1947, **27,** 240–307.

Beach, F. A. *Hormones and Behavior.* New York: Paul Hoeber, 1948.

Beach, F. A. Instinctive behavior: reproductive activities. In S. S. Stevens (Ed.), *Handbook of Experimental Psychology.* New York: Wiley, 1951.

Beach, F. A. Neural and chemical regulation of behavior. In H. F. Harlow and C. N. Woolsey (Eds.), *Biological and Biochemical Bases of Behavior.* Madison, Wisconsin: University of Wisconsin Press, 1958, pp. 263–284.

Beach, F. A. & A. Zitrin. Induction of mating activity in male cats. *Annals of the New York Academy of Sciences,* 1945, **46,** 42–44.

Beach, F. A., A. Zitrin & J. Jaynes. Neural mediation of mating in male cats. II. Contributions of the frontel cortex. *Journal of Experimental Zoology,* 1955, **130,** 381–401.

Beach, F. A., M. W. Conovitz, F. Steinberg & A. C. Goldstein. Experimental inhibition and restoration of mating behavior in male rats. *Journal of Genetic Psychology,* 1956, **89,** 165–181.

Beach, F. A. & H. Fowler. Individual differences in the response of male rats to androgen. *Journal of Comparative and Physiological Psychology,* 1959, **52,** 50–52.

Beecher, H. F. *Measurement of Subjective Responses.* New York: Oxford University Press, 1959.

Belding, H. S., M. B. Macht & M. E. Bader. Indirect peripheral vasodilatation produced by the warming of various body areas. U. S. Army Quartermaster, Res. & Dev. Cen., Natick, Mass.: *Environmental Protection Report No. 132*, June 11, 1948.

Bell, C., G. Sierra, N. Buendia & J. P. Segundo. Sensory properties of neurons in the mesencephalic reticular formation. *Journal of Neurophysiology,* 1964, **27**, 961–987.

Bellows, R. T. & W. P. Van Wagenen. The relationship of polydipsia and polyuria in diabetes insipidus. *Journal of Nervous and Mental Disease,* 1938, **88**, 417–473.

Benjamin, R. N. & K. Akert. Cortical and thalamic areas involved in taste discrimination. *Journal of Comparative Neurology,* 1959, **111**, 231–260.

Benzinger, T. H. On physical heat regulation and the sense of temperature in man. *Proceedings of the National Academy of Sciences,* 1959, **45**, 645–659.

Benzinger, T. H. The sensory receptor organ and quantitative mechanism of human temperature control in warm environment. *Federation Proceedings,* 1960, **19**, 32–41.

Benzinger, T. H. The human thermostat. *Scientific American,* 1961a, **204**, 134–147.

Benzinger, T. H. The quantitative mechanism and the sensory receptor organ of human temperature control in warm environment. *Annals of Internal Medicine,* 1961b, **54**, 685–699.

Benzinger, T. H. The diminution of thermoregulatory sweating during cold-reception at the skin. *Proceedings of the National Academy of Sciences,* 1961c, **47**, 1683–1688.

Benzinger, T. H. Peripheral cold- and central warm-reception, main origins of human thermal discomfort. *Proceedings of the National Academy of Sciences,* 1963, **49**, 832–839.

Benzinger, T. H., A. W. Pratt & C. Kitzinger. The thermostatic control of human metabolic heat production. *Proceedings of the National Academy of Sciences,* 1961, **47**, 730–739.

Berkun, M. M., M. L. Kessen & N. E. Miller. Hunger-reducing effects of food by stomach fistula versus food by mouth measured by a consummatory response. *Journal of Comparative and Physiological Psychology,* 1952, **45**, 550–554.

Berlyne, D. E. *Conflict, Arousal and Curiosity,* New York: McGraw-Hill, 1960.

Bettelheim, B. *The Informed Heart.* New York: The Free Press of Glencoe, 1960.

Bexton, W. H., W. Heron & T. H. Scott. Effects of decreased variation in the sensory environment. *Canadian Journal of Psychology,* 1954, **8**, 70–76.

Bindra, D. *Motivation: A Systematic Reinterpretation.* New York: Ronald Press, 1959.

Birzis, L. & A. Hemingway. Descending brain stem connections controlling shivering in the cat. *Journal of Neurophysiology,* 1956, **19**, 37–43.

Birzis, L. & A. Hemingway. Efferent brain discharge during shivering. *Journal of Neurophysiology,* 1957 **20**, 156–166.

Bishop, M. P., S. T. Eldner & R. G. Heath. Intracranial self-stimulation in man. *Science,* 1963, **140**, 394–395.

Blickenstaff, D. D. Increase of intestinal absorption of water from isomotic saline following pitressin administration. *American Journal of Physiology,* 1954, **179**, 471–472.

Bolles, R. C. *Theory of Motivation.* New York: Harper and Row, 1967.

Bower, G. H. & N. E. Miller. Rewarding and punishing effects from stimulating the same place in the rat's brain. *Journal of Comparative and Physiological Psychology,* 1958, **51**, 669–678.

Brady, J. V. & H. F. Hunt. An experimental approach to the analysis of emotional behavior. *Journal of Psychology,* 1955, **40**, 313–324.

Brady, J. V. The paleocortex and behavioral motivation. In H. R. Harlow and C. N. Woolsey (Eds.), *Biological and Biochemical Bases of Behavior.* Madison, Wisconsin: University of Wisconsin Press, 1958, pp. 193–235.

Brobeck, J. R. Neural control of hunger, appetite and satiety. *Yale Journal of Biology and Medicine,* 1957, **29**, 565–574.

Brobeck, J. R. Food and temperature. *Recent Progress in Hormone Research,* 1960, **16**, 439–446.

Brobeck, J. R. & J. Ranson. Activation of heat loss mechanisms by local heating of the brain. *Journal of Neurophysiology,* 1938, **1**, 101–114.

Brobeck, J. R., J. Tepperman & C. N. H. Long. Experimental hypothalamic hyperphagia in the albino rat. *Yale Journal of Biology and Medicine,* 1943, **15**, 831–853.

Brookhart, J. M., F. L. Dey & S. W. Ranson. The abolition of mating behavior by hypothalamic lesions in guinea pigs. *Endocrinology,* 1941, **28**, 561–565.

Brooks, C. McC., D. N. Marine & E. F. Lambert. A study of the food-feces ratio and of the oxygen consumption of albino rats during various phases of experimentally produced obesity. *American Journal of Physiology,* 1946, **147**, 717–726.

Brown, J. S. *The Motivation of Behavior.* New York: McGraw-Hill, 1961.

Brown, J. S. & I. E. Farber. Emotions conceptualized as intervening variables—with suggestions toward a theory of frustration. *Psychological Bulletin,* 1951, **48**, 465–495.

Brush, F. R. The effects of shock intensity on the acquisition and extinction of an avoidance response in dogs. *Journal of Comparative and Physiological Psychology,* 1957, **50**, 547–552.

Burgess, M. & J. E. Hokanson. Effects of autonomic arousal level, sex and frustration on performance. *Perceptual and Motor Skills,* 1968, **26**, 919–930.

Burton, A. C. & O. G. Edholm. *Man in a Cold Environment.* Baltimore, Maryland: Williams and Wilkins, 1955.

Butler, R. A. Discrimination learning by rhesus monkeys to visual-exploration motivation. *Journal of Comparative and Physiological Psychology,* 1953, **46**, 95–98.

Butler, R. A. & H. F. Harlow. Persistence of visual exploration in monkeys. *Journal of Comparative and Physiological Psychology,* 1954, **47**, 258–263.

Campbell, B. A. & D. Kraeling. Response strength as a function of drive level and amount of drive reduction. *Journal of Experimental Psychology,* 1953, **46**, 173–175.

Cannon, W. B. The James-Lange theory of emotions: a critical examination and an alternative theory. *American Journal of Psychology,* 1927, **39**, 106–124.

Cannon, W. B. *The Wisdom of the Body.* New York: Norton, 1932.

Carr, W. J. The effect of adrenalectomy upon the NaCl taste threshold in rats. *Journal of Comparative and Physiological Psychology,* 1952, **45**, 377–380.

Child, I. L. & I. K. Waterhouse. Frustration and the quality of performance: II. A theoretical statement. *Psychological Review,* 1953, **60**, 127–139.

Chow, K. L., W. C. Dement & S. A. Mitchell, Jr. Effects of lesions of the rostral thalamus on brain waves and behavior in cats. *Electroencephalography and Clinical Neurophysiology,* 1959, **11**, 107–120.

Christian, J. J. The roles of endocrine and behavioral factors in the growth of mammalian populations. In A. Gorbman (Ed.), *Comparative Endocrinology.* Columbia University Symposium, Cold Spring Harbor. New York: Wiley, 1959.

Chun-Wuei Chein & N. E. Miller. Cited in N. E. Miller. Chemical coding of behavior in the brain. *Science,* 1965, 16, 328–338.

Church, R. M. The varied effects of punishment on behavior, *Psychological Review,* 1963, 70, 369–402.

Clark, G. Prepubertal castration in the male chimpanzee, with some effects of replacement therapy. *Growth,* 1945, 9, 327–339.

Cohen, M. J., S. Hagiwara & Y. Zotterman. The response spectrum of taste fibers in the cat: A single fiber analysis. *Acta Physiologica Scandinavica,* 1955, 33, 316–332.

Conn, L. K. & D. P. Crowne. Instigation to aggression, emotional arousal and defensive emulation. *Journal of Personality,* 1964, 32, 163–179.

Coons, W. H. & N. E. Miller. Cited in N. E. Miller. Experiments on motivation. *Science,* 1957, 126, 1271–1278.

Cottle, M. & L. D. Carlson. Turnover of thyroid hormone in cold-exposed rats determined by radioactive iodine studies. *Endocrinology,* 1956, 59, 1–11.

Crosby, E. C. & R. T. Woodburne. The mammalian midbrain and isthmus regions. Part II. The fiber connections. C. The hypothalamo-tegmental pathways. *Journal of Comparative Neurology,* 1951, 94, 1–32.

Danzig, E. R., P. W. Thayer & L. R. Galanter. The effects of a threatening rumor on a disaster-stricken community. Washington, D.C.: National Academy of Sciences, National Research Council, Disaster Research Group, *Disaster Study No. 10,* 1958.

Darwin, C. *Origin of Species.* New York: Modern Library, 1936 edition, 1859.

Delgado, J. M. R. Study of some cerebral structures related to transmission and elaboration of noxious stimulation. *Journal of Neurophysiology,* 1955, 18, 261–275.

Delgado, J. M. R. Cerebral heterostimulation in a monkey colony. *Science,* 1963, 141, 161–163.

Delgado, J. M. R. *Emotions,* Dubuque, Iowa: Wm. C. Brown, 1966.

Delgado, J. M. R., W. W. Roberts & N. E. Miller. Learning motivated by electrical stimulation of the brain. *American Journal of Physiology,* 1954, 179, 587–593.

Delgado, J. M. R. & H. Hamlin. Surface and depth electrography of the frontal lobes in conscious patients. *Electroencephalography and Clinical Neurophysiology,* 1956, 8, 371–384.

Dement, W. C. The effect of dream deprivation. *Science,* 1960, 131, 1705–1707.

Dement, W. C. An essay on dreams. In W. Edwards, H. Lindman, and L. D. Phillips (Eds.), *New Directions in Psychology II.* New York: Holt, Rinehart and Winston, 1965.

Dement, W. C. & N. Kleitman. Cyclic variations in EEG during sleep and their relations to eye movements, body motility, and dreaming. *Electroencephalography and Clinical Neurophysiology,* 1957, 9, 673–690.

Dibner, A. S. Ambiguity and anxiety. *Journal of Abnormal and Social Psychology,* 1958, 56, 165–174.

Doerr, H. O. & J. E. Hokanson. A relation between heart rate and performance in children. *Journal of Personality and Social Psychology,* 1965, 2, 70–76.

Duffy, Elizabeth. The conceptual categories of psychology: a suggestion for revision. *Psychological Review,* 1941, 48, 177–203.

Easterbrook, J. A. The effect of emotion on cue utilization and the organization of behavior. *Psychological Review,* 1959, 66, 183–201.

Efron, D. & J. P. Foley. Gestural behavior and social setting. In T. M. Newcomb and E. L. Hartley (Eds.), *Readings in Social Psychology*. New York: Holt, Rinehart and Winston, 1947.

Ehrlich, A. Neural control of feeding behavior. *Psychological Bulletin*, 1964, **61**, 100–114.

Eidelberg, E., J. C. White & M. A. Brazier. The hippocampal arousal pattern in rabbits. *Experimental Neurology*, 1959, **1**, 483.

Elmadjian, F., J. M. Hope & C. T. Larson. Excretion of epinephrine and norepinephrine under stress. *Recent Progress in Hormone Research*, 1958, **14**, 513.

Epstein, A. N. Reciprocal changes in feeding behavior produced by intrahypothalamic chemical injections. *American Journal of Physiology*, 1960, **199**, 969–974.

Epstein, A. N. & P. Teitelbaum. Regulation of food intake in the absence of taste, smell, and other oropharyngeal sensations. *Journal of Comparative and Physiological Psychology*, 1962, **55**, 753–759.

Epstein, S. The measurement of drive and conflict in humans: theory and experiment. In M. R. Jones (Ed.), *Nebraska Symposium on Motivation*. Lincoln, Nebr.: Univ. of Nebraska Press, 1962.

Estes, W. K. & B. F. Skinner. Some quantative properties of anxiety. *Journal of Psychology*, 1941, **29**, 390–400.

Everett, J. W. The central nervous system and control of reproductive function. In C. W. Lloyd (Ed.), *Human Reproduction and Sexual Behavior*. Philadelphia: Lea and Febiger, 1964, pp. 25–49.

Falk, J. L. Studies on schedule-induced polydipsia. In M. J. Wayner (Ed.), *Thirst: First International Symposium on Thirst in the Regulation of Body Water*. Oxford: Pergamon Press, 1964, pp. 95–116.

Farber, I. E. & K. W. Spence. Complex learning and conditioning as a function of anxiety. *Journal of Experimental Psychology*, 1953, **45**, 120–125.

Farber, I. E., H. F. Harlow & R. J. West. Brainwashing, conditioning, and DDD (debility, depending, and dread). *Sociometry*, 1957, **20**, 271–285.

Fel'berbaum, I. M. Cited in G. Razran. The observable unconscious and the inferable conscious in current Soviet psychophysiology: Interoceptive conditioning, semantic conditioning, and the orienting reflex. *Psychological Review*, 1961, **68**, 81–147.

Fenz, W. D. Conflict and stress as related to physiological activation and sensory, perceptual, and cognitive functioning. *Psychological Monographs*, 1964, **78**, no. 8, (whole no. 585).

Fisher, A. E. Maternal and sexual behavior induced by intracranial chemical stimulation. *Science*, 1956, **124**, 228–229.

Forster, R. E., II & R. K. Macpherson. The regulation of body temperature during fever. *Journal of Physiology*, 1952, **125**, 210–220.

Frazier, J. W. Adrenal participation in conditioned arousal. Unpublished doctoral dissertation, Florida State University, 1966.

Freeman, G. L. The relationship between performance level and bodily activity level. *Journal of Experimental Psychology*, 1940, **26**, 602–608.

Freeman, W. J. & D. D. Davis. Effects on cats of conductive hypothalamic cooling. *American Journal of Physiology*, 1959, **197**, 145–148.

French, Elizabeth, G. Some characteristics of achievement motivation. *Journal of Experimental Psychology*, 1955, **50**, 232–236.

French, J. D., R. Hernandez-Peon & R. B. Livingston. Projections from cortex to cephalic brain stem (reticular formation) in monkey. *Journal of Neurophysiology*, 1955, **18**, 74–95.

Freud, S. The unconscious (1915). In *Collected Papers of Sigmund Freud*, vol. IV (Riviere, Joan, transl.). London: Hogarth Press, 1949.

Funkenstein, D. H., S. H. King & M. E. Drolette. *Mastery of Stress*. Cambridge, Mass.: Harvard Univ. Press, 1957.

Fuster, J. M. Effects of stimulation of brain stem on tachistoscopic perception. *Science*, 1958, **127**, 150.

Galambos, R. Suppression of auditory nerve activity by stimulation of efferent fibers to the cochlea. *Journal of Neurophysiology*, 1956, **19**, 424–437.

Galambos, R. & G. S. Sheatz. An electroencephalograph study of classical conditioning. *American Journal of Physiology*, 1962, **203**, 173–184.

Gilbert, G. J. & G. H. Glaser. On the nervous system integration of water and salt metabolism. *Archives of Neurology* (Chicago), 1961, **5**, 179–196.

Gilman, A. The relation between blood osmotic pressure, fluid distribution and voluntary water intake. *American Journal of Physiology*, 1937, **120**, 323–328.

Goy, R. W. Reproductive behavior in mammals. In C. W. Lloyd (Ed.), *Human Reproduction and Sexual Behavior*. Philadelphia: Lea and Febiger, 1964, pp. 409–441.

Grande, F., J. T. Anderson & H. L. Taylor. Effect of restricted water intake on urine nitrogen output in man on a low calorie diet devoid of protein. *Journal of Applied Physiology*, 1957, **10**, 430–435.

Granit, R. Centrifugal and antidromic effects on ganglion cells of retina. *Journal of Neurophysiology*, 1955, **18**, 388–411.

Grastyan, E., K. Lissak, I. Madarasz & H. Donhoffer. Hippocampal electrical activity during the development of conditioned reflexes. *Electroencephalography and Clinical Neurophysiology*, 1959, **11**, 409–430.

Green, J. D. & A. Arduini. Hippocampal electrical activity in arousal. *Journal of Neurophysiology*, 1954, **17**, 533–557.

Griffiths, W. J. & T. J. Gallagher. Differential dietary choices of albino rats occasioned by swimming. *Science*, 1953, **118**, 780.

Grinker, R. R. & J. P. Spiegel. *Men Under Stress*. New York: McGraw-Hill Book Company, 1945.

Grossman, S. P. Eating or drinking elicited by direct adrenergic or cholinergic stimulation of hypothalamus. *Science*, 1960, **132**, 301–302.

Grossman, S. P. Cited in N. E. Miller. Motivation effects of brain stimulation and drugs. *Federation Proceedings*, 1960, **19**, 846–854.

Grossman, S. P. *A Textbook of Physiological Psychology*. New York: John Wiley and Sons, 1967.

Grossman, S. P. & A. Rechtschaffen. Cited in S. P. Grossman, *A Textbook of Physiological Psychology*. New York: John Wiley and Sons, 1967, p. 372.

Hagbarth, K. E. & D. I. B. Kerr. Central influences on spinal afferent conduction. *Journal of Neurophysiology*, 1954, **17**, 295–307.

Hall, C. S. The genetics of behavior. In S. S. Stevens (Ed.), *Handbook of Experimental Psychology*. New York: John Wiley and Sons, 1951.

Halpern, B. P. Gustatory responses in the medulla oblongata of the rat. Unpublished doctoral dissertation, Brown University, 1959.

Haner, C. F. & P. A. Brown. Clarification of the instigation to action concept in the frustration-aggression hypothesis. *Journal of Abnormal and Social Psychology*, 1955, **51**, 204–206.

Hardy, J. D., H. G. Wolff & H. Goodell. *Pain Sensations and Reactions*. Baltimore: Williams and Wilkins, 1952.

Hardy, J. D. The physiology of temperature regulation. U.S. Navy Bureau of Medicine and Surgery, *Task MR 995.15–2002.1*, 1960.

Harlow, H. F. The nature of love. *American Psychologist*, 1958, **13**, 673–685.

Harlow, H. F. The heterosexual affectional system in monkeys. *American Psychologist*, 1962, **17**, 1–9.

Harlow, H. F., Margaret K. Harlow & D. R. Meyer. Learning motivated by a manipulation drive. *Journal of Experimental Psychology*, 1950. **40**, 228–234.

Harlow, H. F. & R. R. Zimmermann. Affectional responses in the infant monkey. *Science*, 1959, **130**, 421–432.

Harlow, H. F. & Margaret K. Harlow. Social deprivation in monkeys. *Scientific American*, 1962, **207**, 136–146.

Harris, G. W. *Neural Control of the Pituitary Gland*. London: Edward Arnold, 1955*a*.

Harris, G. W. The function of the pituitary stalk. *Bulletin of Johns Hopkins Hospital*, 1955*b*, **97**, 358–375.

Hart, J. S. Effects of temperature and work on metabolism, body temperature and insulation: Results with mice. *Canadian Journal of Zoology*, 1952, **30**, 90–98.

Hebb, D. O. The role of neurological ideas in psychology. *Journal of Personality*, 1951, **20**, 39–55.

Hemingway, A. Alaskan Air Command Technical Note, *AAL–TN–40*, 1957.

Hemingway, A., T. Rasmussen, H. Wickoff & A. T. Rasmussen. Effects of heating hypothalamus of dogs by diathermy. *Journal of Neurophysiology*, 1940, **3**, 329–338.

Henry, P., H. Cohen, B. Stadel, J. Stulce, J. Ferguson, T. Wagener & W. C. Dement. CSF transfer from REM deprived cats to nondeprived recipients. Washington, D.C.: APSS, 1965.

Henschel, A. Minimal water requirements under conditions of heat and work. In M. J. Wayner (Ed.), *Thirst: First International Symposium on Thirst in the Regulation of Body Water*. Oxford: Pergamon Press, 1964, pp. 19–30.

Hensel, H. and Y. Zotterman. The response of the cold receptors to constant cooling. *Acta Physiologica Scandinavica*, 1951, **22**, 96–105.

Hensel, H. & K. A. Boman. Afferent impulses in cutaneous sensory nerves in human subjects. *Journal of Neurophysiology*, 1960, **23**, 564–578.

Herberg, L. J. Seminal ejaculation following positively reinforcing electrical stimulation of the rat hypothalamus. *Journal of Comparative and Physiological Psychology*, 1963, **56**, 679–685.

Hernandez-Peon, R. Reticular mechanisms of sensory control. In W. A. Rosenblith (Ed.), *Sensory Communication*, Cambridge, Mass.: M.I.T. Press, 1961.

Hernandez-Peon, R. *Neurophysiological Mechanisms of Wakefulness and Sleep*. Washington, D.C.: XVII, International Congress of Psychology, 1963.

Hernandez-Peon, R., H. Scherrer & M. Jouvet. Modification of electrical activity in cochlear nucleus during "attention" in unanesthetized cats. *Science*, 1956, **123**, 331–332.

Hernandez-Peon, R., C. Guzman-Flores, M. Alcaraz & A. Fernandez-Guardiola. Sensory transmission in visual pathway during "attention" in unanesthetized cats. *Acta Neurologica Latin-America*, 1957, **3**, 1-8.

Hernandez-Peon, R., A. Lavin, C. Aleocercuaron & J. P. Marcelin. Electrical activity of the olfactory bulb during wakefulness and sleep. *Electroencephalography and Clinical Neurophysiology*, 1960, **12**, 41–58.

Heron, W., B. K. Doane & T. H. Scott. Visual disturbances after prolonged perceptual isolation. *Canadian Journal of Psychology*, 1956, **10**, 13–18.

Hess, W. R. *Diencephalon—Autonomic and Extra-pyramidal Functions*. New York: Grune and Stratton, 1954.

Hetherington, A. W. & S. W. Ranson. Hypothalamic lesions and adiposity in the rat. *Anatomical Record*, 1940, **78**, 149–172.

Hetherington, A. W. & S. W. Ranson. Effect of early hypophysectomy on hypothalamic obesity. *Endocrinology*, 1942, **31**, 30–34.

Higgins, J. W., G. F. Mahl, J. M. R. Delgado & H. Hamlin. Behavioral changes during intracerebral electrical stimulation. *Archives of Neurology and Psychiatry*, 1956, **76**, 399–419.

Hilgard, E. R. *Theories of Learning* (2d ed.). New York: Appleton Century-Crofts, 1956.

Hinde, R. A. *Animal Behavior*. New York: McGraw-Hill Book Company, 1966.

Hoebel, B. G. & P. Teitelbaum. Hypothalamic control of feeding and self-stimulation. *Science*, 1962, **135**, 375–377.

Hokanson, J. E. Vascular and psychogalvanic effects of experimentally aroused anger. *Journal of Personality*, 1961, **29**, 30–39.

Hokanson, J. E. & M. Burgess. The effects of status, type of frustration, and aggression on vascular processes. *Journal of Abnormal and Social Psychology*, 1962, **65**, 232–237.

Hokanson, J. E. & M. Burgess. Effects of physiological arousal level, frustration, and task complexity on performance. *Journal of Abnormal and Social Psychology*, 1964, **68**, 698–702.

Hokanson, J. E., K. R. Willers & Elizabeth Koropsak. The modification of autonomic responses during aggressive interchange. *Journal of Personality* 1968, **36**, 386–404.

Holmes, J. H. & M. I. Gregerson. Observations on drinking induced by hypertonic solutions. *American Journal of Physiology*, 1950, **162**, 326–337.

Holmes, J. H. & L. J. Cizek. Observations on sodium chloride depletion in the dog. *American Journal of Physiology*, 1951, **164**, 407–414.

Horvath, S. M., G. B. Spurr, B. K. Hutt & L. H. Hamilton. Metabolic cost of shivering. *Journal of Applied Physiology*, 1956, **8**, 595–602.

Houghten, F. C., W. W. Teague, W. E. Miller & W. P. Yant. Thermal exchanges between the human body and its atmospheric environment. *American Journal of Physiology*, 1929, **88**, 386–406.

Hull, C. L. Mind, mechanism, and adaptive behavior. *Psychological Review*, 1937, **44**, 1–32.

Hull, C. L. *Principles of Behavior*. New York: Appleton Century-Crofts, 1943.

Hunt, H. F. & J. V. Brady. Some effects of electroconvulsive shock on a conditioned emotional response ("anxiety"). *Journal of Comparative and Physiological Psychology*, 1951, **44**, 88–98.

Hutchinson, R., R. E. Ulrich & N. H. Azrin. Effects of age and related factors on reflexive aggression. *Journal of Comparative and Physiological Psychology*, 1965, **59**, 365–369.

Iampietro, P. F., M. J. Fregley & E. R. Buskirk. Maintenance of body temperature of restrained adrenalectomized rats exposed to cold: Effect of adrenal cortical hormones. *Canadian Journal of Biochemistry and Physiology*, 1956, **34**, 721–729.

Janis, I. L. *Air War and Emotional Stress*. New York: McGraw-Hill Book Company, 1951.

Janis, I. L. *Psychological Stress*. New York: Wiley, 1958.

Janis, I. L. Psychological effects of warnings. In G. W. Baker and D. W. Chapman (Eds.), *Man and Society in Disaster*. New York: Basic Books, 1962.

Jasper, H. H. Reticular-cortical systems and theories of the integrative action of the brain. In H. F. Harlow and C. N. Woolsey, *Biological and Biochemical Bases of Behavior*. Madison, Wisconsin: University of Wisconsin Press, 1958, pp. 37–62.

Jasper, H. H. Unspecific thalamocortical relations. In J. Field, H. W. Magoun, and V. E. Hall (Eds.), *Handbook of Physiology*, Vol. II. Baltimore: Williams and Wilkins, 1960.

Jouvet, M. & R. Hernandez-Peon. Mechanisms neurophysiologiques concernant l'habituation, l'attention et le conditionnement. In H. Fischgold and H. Gastaut (Eds.), Conditionement et reactivité en electroencephalographie. *Electroencephalography and Clinical Neurophysiology*, 1957, **39**, Supplement 6.

Jouvet, M. Paradoxical sleep—a study of its nature and mechanisms. In K. Akert, C. Bally, and J. P. Schade (Eds.), *Sleep Mechanisms*, Vol. 18. Amsterdam: Elsevier, 1965.

Kaada, B. R. & N. B. Johannessen. Generalized electrocortical activation by cortical stimulation in the cat. *Electroencephalography and Clinical Neurophysiology*, 1960, **12**, 567–573.

Kamin, L. J. The delay-of-punishment gradient. *Journal of Comparative and Physiological Psychology*, 1959, **52**, 434–437.

Kamin, L. J. & R. E. Schaub. Effects of conditioned stimulus intensity on the conditioned emotional response. *Journal of Comparative and Physiological Psychology*, 1963, **56**, 502–507.

Kamiya, J. Behavioral, subjective, and physiological aspects of drowsiness and sleep. In D. W. Fiske, and S. R. Maddi (Eds.), *Functions of Varied Experience*. Homewood: Dorsey, 1961.

Kanter, G. S. Excretion and drinking after self loading in dogs. *American Journal of Physiology*, 1953, **174**, 87–93.

Karsh, Eileen. Effects of number of rewarded trials and intensity of punishment on running speed. *Journal of Comparative and Physiological Psychology*, 1962, **55**, 44–51.

Kassil, V. G. Cited in G. Razran. The observable unconscious and the inferable conscious in current Soviet psychophysiology: Interoceptive conditioning, semantic conditioning, and the orienting reflex. *Psychological Review*, 1961, **68**, 81–147.

Keller, A. D. Thermal regulation. *Physical Therapy Review*, 1950, **30**, 511–519.

Kellogg, V. Some silkworm moth reflexes. *Biological Bulletin, Woods Hole*, 1907, **12**, 152–154.

Kennedy, G. C. The role of depot fat in the hypothalamic control of food intake in the rat. *Proceedings of the Royal Society* (London), B, 1952, **140**, 578–592.

Kenshalo, D. R. & J. P. Nafe. A quantitative theory of feeling: 1960. *Psychological Review*, 1962, **69**, 17–33.

Kinsey, A. C., W. B. Pomeroy & C. E. Martin. *Sexual Behavior in the Human Male*. Philadelphia: Saunders, 1948.

Kleitman, N. *Sleep and Wakefulness* (rev. ed.). Chicago: University of Chicago Press, 1963.

Kluver, H. & P. C. Bucy. Preliminary analysis of functions of the temporal lobes in monkeys. *Archives of Neurology and Psychiatry*, 1939, **42**, 979–1000.

Koller, G. Hormonale und psychische Steurung beim Nestbau weisser Mäuse. *Zoologischer Anzeiger* (Suppl.), 1956, **19**, 123–132.

Lacey, J. I. The evaluation of autonomic responses: toward a general solution. *Annals of the New York Academy of Sciences,* 1956, **67,** 123–164.

Lacey, J. I. & B. C. Lacey. Verification and extension of the principle of autonomic response stereotypy. *American Journal of Psychology,* 1958, **71,** 50.

Lacey, J. I., J. Kagan, B. C. Lacey & H. A. Moss. The visceral level: situational determinants and behavioral correlates of autonomic response patterns. In P. H. Knapp (Ed.), *Expressions of the Emotions in Man.* New York: International Universities Press, 1963.

Landauer, T. K. Two hypotheses concerning the biochemical basis of memory. *Psychological Review,* 1964, **71,** 167–179.

Lansing, R. W., E. Schwartz & D. E. Lindsley. Reaction time and EEG activation under alerted and nonalerted conditions. *Journal of Experimental Psychology,* 1959, **58,** 1–7.

Lazarus, R. S. *Psychological Stress and the Coping Process.* New York: McGraw-Hill Book Company, 1966.

Lazarus, R. S., J. Deese & S. F. Osler. The effects of psychological stress upon performance. *Psychological Bulletin,* 1952, **49,** 293–317.

Lazarus, R. S., J. C. Spiesman, A. M. Mordkoff & L. A. Davison. A laboratory study of psychological stress produced by a motion picture film. *Psychological Monographs,* 1962, **76,** no. 344 (whole no. 553).

Lazarus, R. S., E. M. Opton, M. S. Nomikos & N. O. Rankin. The principle of short-circuiting of threat: further evidence. *Journal of Personality,* 1965, **33,** 622–635.

Levi, L. The urinary output of adrenalin and nonadrenalin during pleasant and unpleasant emotional states: a preliminary report. *Psychosomatic Medicine,* 1965, **27,** 80–85.

Lilly, J. C. Mental effects of reduction of ordinary levels of physical stimuli on intact healthy person. *Psychiatric Research Reports,* 1956, **5,** 1–9.

Lindsley, D. B. Emotion. In S. S. Stevens (Ed.), *Handbook of Experimental Psychology.* New York: John Wiley and Sons, 1951, pp. 437–516.

Lindsley, D. B., L. H. Schreiner, W. B. Knowles & H. W. Magoun. Behavioral and EEG changes following chronic brain stem lesions in the cat. *Electroencephalography and Clinical Neurophysiology,* 1950, **2,** 483–498.

Lindzey, G., D. T. Lykken & H. D. Winston. Infantile trauma, genetic factors and adult temperment. *Journal of Abnormal and Social Psychology,* 1960, **61,** 7–14.

Lloyd, C. W. & J. H. Leatham. Reproductive cycles, oogenesis, ovulation and conception. In C. W. Lloyd (Ed.), *Human Reproduction and Sexual Behavior.* Philadelphia: Lea and Febiger, 1964, pp. 92–101.

Loewenstein, W. R. Modulation of cutaneous mechanoreceptors by sympathetic stimulation. *Journal of Physiology* (London), 1956, **132,** 40.

Lorenz, K. Comparative study of behavior (1939). In Claire H. Schiller (Ed.), *Instinctive Behavior.* New York: International Universities Press, 1957.

Lorenz, K. *On Aggression* (translated by Marjorie K. Wilson). New York: Harcourt, Brace, and World, 1966.

Lucas, J. D. The interactive effects of anxiety, failure, and intraserial duplication. *American Journal of Psychology,* 1952, **65,** 59–66.

Luria, A. R. *The Nature of Human Conflicts.* New York: Liveright, 1932.

MacFarlane, W. V. & K. W. Robinson. Decrease in human excretion of 17-ketogenic steroids and 17-ketosteroids with increasing ambient temperature. *Journal of Applied Physiology,* 1957, **11,** 199–200.

MacLean, P. D. & D. W. Ploog. Cerebral representation of penile erection. *Journal of Neurophysiology,* 1962, **25,** 30–55.

MacLean, P. D., R. H. Denniston & S. Dua. Further studies on cerebral representation of penile erection: caudal thalamus, midbrain, and pons. *Journal of Neurophysiology*, 1963, **26**, 273–293.

Magoun, H. W. Non-specific brain mechanisms. In H. F. Harlow and C. N. Woolsey (Eds.), *Biological and Biochemical Bases of Behavior*. Madison, Wisconsin: University of Wisconsin Press, 1958, pp. 25–36.

Magoun, H. W., F. Harrison, J. R. Brobeck & S. W. Ranson. Activation of heat loss mechanisms by local heating of the brain. *Journal of Neurophysiology*, 1938, **1**, 101–114.

Maier, N. R. F. Frustration theory: Restatement and extension. *Psychological Review*, 1956, **63**, 370–388.

Malmo, R. B. Measurement of drive: an unsolved problem in psychology. In M. R. Jones (Ed.), *Nebraska Symposium on Motivation*. Lincoln, Nebraska: University of Nebraska Press, 1958, pp. 229–264.

Malmo, R. B. Activation: a neurophysiological dimension. *Psychological Review*, 1959, **66**, 367–386.

Malmo, R. B., C. Shagass, J. F. Davis & M. Eng. Electromyographic studies of muscular tension in psychiatric patients under stress. *Journal of Clinical and Experimental Psychopathology*, 1951, **12**, 45–66.

Margules, D. L. & J. Olds. Identical "feeding" and "rewarding" systems in the lateral hypothalamus of rats. *Science*, 1962, **135**, 374–475.

Masters, W. H. & V. E. Johnson. *Human Sexual Response*, Boston: Little, Brown & Co., 1966.

Matsumoto, J. & M. Jouvet. Effet de reserpine, DOPA, et 5 HTP, sur les deuz etats de sommeil, *Comptes Rendus des Seances de la Societe de Biologie*, 1964, **158**, 2037.

Mayer, J. The glucostatic theory of regulation of food intake and the problem of obesity. *Bulletin of the New England Medical Center*, 1952, **14**, 43–49.

Mayer, J. Regulation of energy intake and the body weight. The glucostatic theory and the lipostatic hypothesis. *Annals of the New York Academy of Science*, 1955, **63**, 15–43.

Mayer, J. & N. B. Marshall. Specificity of goldthioglucose for ventromedial hypothalamic lesions and hyperphagia. *Nature* (London), 1956, **178**, 1399–1400.

McDougall, W. *An Introduction to Social Psychology* (5th ed.). London: Methuen, 1912.

Melzack, R. & P. D. Wall. Pain mechanisms: A new theory. *Science*, 1965, **150**, 971–979.

Melzack, R. & K. L. Casey. Sensory, motivational and central control determinants of pain. In D. R. Kenshalo (Ed.), *International Symposium on Skin Senses*. Springfield: Thomas, 1967.

Michael, R. P. Estrogen-sensitive neurons and sexual behavior in female cats. *Science*, 1962, **136**, 322–323.

Miller, N. E. Studies of fear as an acquired drive: Fear as motivation and fear-reduction as reinforcement in the learning of new responses. *Journal of Experimental Psychology*, 1948, **38**, 89–101.

Miller, N. E. Experiments on motivation. *Science*, 1957, **126**, 1271–1278.

Miller, N. E. Liberalization of basic S-R concepts: extensions to conflict behavior, motivation, and social learning. In S. Koch (Ed.), *Psychology: a Study of a Science*, Vol. II. New York: McGraw-Hill Book Company, 1959.

Miller, N. E. Learning resistance to pain and fear: Effects of overlearning, exposure, and rewarded exposure in context. *Journal of Experimental Psychology*, 1960, 60, 137–145.

Miller, N. E. Implications for theories of reinforcement. In D. E. Sheer (Ed.), *Electrical Stimulation of the Brain*. Austin: University of Texas Press, 1961.

Miller, N. E. Chemical coding of behavior in the brain. *Science*, 1965, 16, 328–338.

Miller, N. E. & J. Dollard. *Social Learning and Imitation*. New Haven: Yale University Press, 1941.

Miller, N. E., C. J. Bailey & J. A. F. Stevenson. Decreased "hunger" but increased food intake resulting from hypothalamic lesion. *Science*, 1950, 112, 256–259.

Montague, E. K. The role of anxiety in serial rote learning, *Journal of Experimental Psychology*, 1953, 45, 91–95.

Morgan, C. T. *Physiological Psychology*. New York: McGraw-Hill Book Company, 1965.

Morgane, P. J. Alterations in feeding and drinking behavior of rats with lesions in globi pallidi. *American Journal of Physiology*, 1961a, 201, 420–428.

Morgane, P. J. Distinct "feeding" and "hunger motivating" systems in the lateral hypothalamus of the rat. *Science*, 1961b, 133, 887–888.

Morgane, P. J. Evidence of a "hunger motivational" system in the lateral hypothalamus of the rat. *Nature* (London), 1961c, 191, 672–674.

Morgane, P. J. Limbic-hypothalamic-midbrain interaction in thirst and thirst motivated behavior. In M. J. Wayner (Ed.), *Thirst: First International Symposium on Thirst in the Regulation of Body Water*. Oxford: Pergamon Press, 1964, pp. 429–455.

Moruzzi, G. & H. W. Magoun. Brain stem reticular formation and activation of the EEG. *Electroencephalography and Clinical Neurophysiology*, 1949, 1, 445–473.

Mowrer, O. H. An experimental analogue of "regression" with incidental observations on "reaction formation." *Journal of Abnormal and Social Psychology*, 1940, 35, 56–87.

Murgatroyd, D., A. D. Keller & J. D. Hardy. Warmth discrimination in the dog after hypothalamic ablation. *American Journal of Physiology*, 1958, 195, 276–284.

Nakayama, T., J. S. Eisenman & J. D. Hardy. Single unit activity of anterior hypothalamus during local heating. *Science*, 1961, 134, 560–561.

Nissen, J. Instinct as seen by a psychologist. In W. C. Allee, H. W. Nissen, and M. F. Nimkoff, A re-examination of the concept of instinct. *Psychological Review*, 1953, 60, 287–297.

Ogawa, T. Midbrain reticular influences upon single neurons in lateral geniculate nucleus. *Science*, 1963, 139, 343–344.

O'Kelly, L. I. & J. L. Falk. Water regulation in the rat: II. The effects of preloads of water and sodium chloride on the bar-pressing performance of thirsty rats. *Journal of Comparative and Physiological Psychology*, 1958, 51, 88–25.

Olds, J. Self-stimulation of the brain. *Science*, 1958a, 127, 315–324.

Olds, J. Adaptive functions of the paleocortex. In H. Harlow and C. Woolsey (Eds.), *Biological and Biochemical Bases of Behavior*. Madison, Wisconsin: University of Wisconsin Press, 1958b.

Olds, J. Differentiation of reward systems in the brain by self-stimulation techniques. In E. R. Ramsey and D. S. O'Doherty (Eds.), *Electrical Studies on the Unanesthetized Brain*. New York: Paul Hoeber, 1960.

Olds, J. Differential effects of drive and drugs on self-stimulation at different brain sites. In D. E. Sheer (Ed.), *Electrical Stimulation of the Brain.* Austin, Texas: University of Texas Press, 1961.

Olds, J. S. & P. Milner. Positive reinforcement produced by electrical stimulation of septal area and other regions of the rat brain. *Journal of Comparative and Physiological Psychology,* 1954, **47**, 419–427.

Olds, J. S. & M. E. Olds. Interference and learning in paleocortical systems. In Delafresnaye (Ed.), *Brain Mechanisms and Learning.* Oxford: Blackwell Scientific Publications, 1961, pp. 153–187.

Olds, J. S. & M. E. Olds. Drives, rewards and the brain. In *New Directions in Psychology II.* New York: Holt, Rinehart and Winston, 1965, pp. 329–410.

Olds, M. E. & J. S. Olds. Approach-avoidance analysis of rat diencephalon. *Journal of Comparative Neurology,* 1963, **120**, 259–295.

Paintal, A. S. A study of right and left atrial receptors. *Journal of Physiology,* 1953, **120**, 596–610.

Paintal, A. S. A study of gastric stretch receptors. Their role in the peripheral mechanism of satiation of hunger and thirst. *Journal of Physiology,* 1954, **126**, 255–270.

Palestini, M., A. Davidovitch & R. Hernandez-Peon. Functional significance of centrifugal influences upon the retina. *Acta Neurologica Latin-America,* 1959, **5**, 113–131.

Penfield, W. & H. Jasper. *Epilepsy, and the Functional Anatomy of the Human Brain.* Boston: Little, Brown, 1954.

Pfaffmann, C. The sensory and motivating properties of the sense of taste. In M. R. Jones (Ed.), *Nebraska Symposium on Motivation.* Lincoln, Nebraska: University of Nebraska Press, 1961, pp. 71–104.

Pfaffmann, C. & J. K. Bare. Gustatory nerve discharges in normal and adrenalectomized rats. *Journal of Comparative and Physiological Psychology,* 1950, **43**, 320–324.

Prescott, R. G. W. Estrous cycle in the rat: effects on self-stimulation behavior. *Science,* 1966, **152**, 796–797.

Purdue Opinion Panel. Youth's attitudes toward courtship and marriage. *Report of Poll No. 62,* 1961.

Ranson, S. W. Somnolence caused by hypothalamic lesions in the monkey. *Archives of Neurology and Psychiatry,* 1939, **41**, 1–23.

Ranson, S. W., H. Kabat & H. W. Magoun. Autonomic response to electrical stimulation of hypothalamus, preoptic region and septum. *American Medical Association Archives of Neurology and Psychiatry,* 1934, **33**, 467–474.

Rasmussen, G. L. Further observations of the efferent cochlear bundle. *Journal of Comparative Neurology,* 1953, **99**, 61.

Razran, G. The observable unconscious and the inferable conscious in current Soviet psychophysiology: Interoceptive conditioning, semantic conditioning, and the orienting reflex. *Psychological Review,* 1961, **68**, 81–147.

Reynolds, R. W. The relationship between stimulation voltage and hypothalamic self-stimulation in the rat. *Journal of Comparative and Physiological Psychology,* 1958, **51**, 193–198.

Reynolds, R. W. Ventromedial hypothalamic lesions without hyperphagia. *American Journal of Physiology,* 1963, **204**, 60–62.

Richter, C. P. Mineral appetite of parathyroidectomized rats. *American Journal of Medical Science,* 1939, **198**, 9–16.

Richter, C. P. Physiological psychology. *Annual Review of Physiology,* 1942, **4**, 561–574.

Richter, C. P. Alcohol, beer and wines as foods. *Quarterly Journal of Studies on Alcohol*, 1953, **14**, 525–539.

Richter, C. P. & J. R. Eckert. Mineral metabolism of adrenalectomized rats studied by the appetite method. *Endocrinology*, 1938, **22**, 214–224.

Richter, C. P. & E. C. Schmidt. Increased fat and decreased carbohydrate appetite of pancreatomized rats. *Endocrinology*, 1941, **28**, 179–192.

Ring, G. C. Thyroid stimulation by cold. *American Journal of Physiology*, 1939, **125**, 244–250.

Roberts, C. L., M. H. Marx & G. Collier. Light onset and light offset as reinforcers for the albino rat. *Journal of Comparative and Physiological Psychology*, 1958, **51**, 575–579.

Sarason, S. B. & G. Mandler. Some correlates of test anxiety. *Journal of Abnormal and Social Psychology*, 1952, **47**, 810–817.

Sarason, S. B., G. Mandler & P. C. Craighill. The effect of differential instructions on anxiety and learning. *Journal of Abnormal and Social Psychology*, 1952, **47**, 561–565.

Sarason, I. G. Empirical findings and theoretical problems in the use of anxiety scales. *Psychological Bulletin*, 1960, **57**, 403–415.

Sawyer, C. J. Reproductive behavior. In J. Field, H. W. Magoun, and V. E. Hall (Eds.), *Handbook of Physiology*, Vol. II. Baltimore: Williams and Wilkins, 1960.

Sawyer, C. H. & B. Robinson. Separate hypothalamic areas controlling pituitary gonadotrophic function and mating behavior in female cats and rabbits. *Journal of Clinical Endocrinology*, 1956, **16**, 914.

Schachter, S. & J. E. Singer. Cognitive, social, and physiological determinants of emotional state. *Psychological Review*, 1962, **69**, 379–399.

Schaeffer, R. W. & J. C. Diehl. Collateral water drinking in rats maintained on FR food reinforcement schedules. *Psychonomic Science*, 1966, **4**, 257–258.

Scheibel, M. E. & A. B. Scheibel. Structural substrates for integrative patterns in the brainstem reticular core. In H. H. Jasper, L. D. Proctor, R. S. Knighton, W. C. Noshay and R. T. Costello (Eds.), *The Reticular Formation of the Brain*. Boston: Little, Brown, 1958.

Schreiner, L. H. & A. Kling. Behavioral changes following rhinencephalic injury in cat. *Journal of Neurophysiology*, 1953, **16**, 643.

Schreiner, L. H. & A. Kling. Effects of castration on hypersexual behavior induced by rhinencephalic injury in cat. *Archives of Neurology and Psychiatry*, 1954, **72**, 180.

Schreiner, L. H. & A. Kling. Rhinencephalon and behavior, *American Journal of Physiology*, 1956, **184**, 486.

Schwartz, M. & F. A. Beach. Effects of adrenalectomy upon mating behavior in male dogs. *American Psychologist*, 1954, **9**, 467–468.

Scott, E. M. & Eleanor Quint. Self selection of diet. III. Appetites for B vitamins. *Journal of Nutrition*, 1946, **32**, 285–292.

Scott, J. P. & M. S. Charles. Genetic differences in dogs: a case of magnification by thresholds and by habit formations. *Journal of Genetic Psychology*, 1954, **84**, 175–188.

Selye, H. A syndrome produced by diverse nocious agents. *Nature*, 1936, **138**, 32.

Selye, H. *The Physiology and Pathology of Exposure to Stress*. Montreal: Acta, 1950.

Selye, H. *The Stress of Life*. New York: McGraw-Hill Book Company, 1956.

Selye, H. *The Chemical Prevention of Cardiac Damage*. New York: Ronald Press, 1958.

Sem-Jacobsen, C. W. Depth electrographic stimulation and treatment of patients with Parkinson's disease including neurosurgical technique. *Acta Neurologica Scandinavica,* 1965, **41**, Suppl. 13.

Sem-Jacobsen, C. W. & A. Torkildsen. In E. R. Ramsey and D. S. O'Doherty (Eds.), *Electrical Studies on the Unanesthetized Brain.* New York: Paul Hoeber, 1960.

Seward, J. P., A. A. Uyeda & J. Olds. Resistance to extinction following cranial self-stimulation. *Journal of Comparative and Physiological Psychology,* 1959, **52**, 294–299.

Sharma, K. N., B. K. Anand, S. Dua & B. Singh. Role of stomach in regulation of activities of hypothalamic feeding centers. *American Journal of Physiology,* 1961, **201**, 593–598.

Sharpless, S. & H. H. Jasper. Habituation of the arousal reaction. *Brain,* 1956, **79**, 655–680.

Sheffield, F. D. & T. B. Roby. Reward value of a non-nutritive sweet taste. *Journal of Comparative and Physiological Psychology,* 1950, **43**, 471–481.

Sheffield, F. D., J. J. Wulff & R. Backer. Reward value of copulation without sex drive reduction. *Journal of Comparative and Physiological Psychology,* 1951, **44**, 3-8.

Sheffield, F. D., T. B. Roby & B. A. Campbell. Drive reduction versus consummatory behavior as determinants of reinforcement. *Journal of Comparative and Physiological Psychology,* 1954, **47**, 349–354.

Shimazu, H., Yanagisawa & B. Garoutte. Corticopyramidal influences on thalamic somatosensory transmission in the cat. *Japanese Journal of Physiology,* 1965, **15**, 101–124.

Sidman, J., J. W. Mason, J. V. Brady & J. Thach. Quantitative relations between avoidance behavior and pituitary, adrenal cortical activity. *Journal of Experimental Analysis of Behavior,* 1962, **5**, 353–362.

Skinner, B. F. *The Behavior of Organisms: An Experimental Analysis.* New York: Appleton-Century-Crofts, 1938.

Skinner, B. F. *Science and Human Behavior.* New York: Macmillan, 1953.

Smith, R. W. & S. M. McCann. Alterations in food and water intake after hypothalamic lesions in the rat. *American Journal of Physiology,* 1962, **203**, 366–370.

Snyder, F. Dream recall, respiratory variability and depth of sleep. Address, Symposium on Dreams, American Psychiatric Association, 1960.

Snyder, F. Progress in the new biology of dreaming. *Archives of General Psychiatry,* 1963, **8**, 381–391.

Solomon, R. L. & L. C. Wynne. Traumatic avoidance learning: the outcomes of several extinction procedures with dogs. *Journal of Abnormal and Social Psychology,* 1953, **48**, 291–302.

Spence, K. W. *Behavior Theory and Conditioning.* New Haven, Connecticut: Yale University Press, 1956.

Spence, K. W. A theory of emotionally bases drive (D) and its relation to performance in simple learning situations. *American Psychologist,* 1958, **13**, 131–141.

Spencer, H. *First Principles.* London: Williams and Norgate, 1862.

Spencer, H. *Principles of Psychology* (3d ed.). London: Williams and Norgate, 1880.

Stein, L. Secondary reinforcement established with subcortical stimulation. *Science,* 1958, **127**, 466–467.

Stein, L. & O. S. Ray. Self-regulation of brain stimulating current intensity in the rat. *Science,* 1959, **130**, 570–572.

Stellar, E., R. Hyman & S. Samet. Gastric factors controlling water and salt-solution drinking. *Journal of Comparative and Physiological Psychology,* 1954, **47**, 220–226.

Stennett, R. G. The relationship of performance level to level of arousal. *Journal of Experimental Psychology*, 1957, **54**, 54–61.

Teitelbaum, P. Random and food-directed activity in hyperphagic and normal rats. *Journal of Comparative and Physiological Psychology*, 1957, **50**, 486–490.

Teitelbaum, P. Disturbances in feeding and drinking behavior after hypothalamic lesions. In M. R. Jones (Ed.), *Nebraska Symposium on Motivation*. Lincoln, Nebraska: University of Nebraska Press, 1961, pp. 39–62.

Teitelbaum, P. Appetite. *Proceedings of the American Philosophical Society*, 1964, **108**, 464–470.

Teitelbaum, P. & E. Stellar. Recovery from the failure to eat produced by hypothalamic lesions. *Science*, 1954, **120**, 894–895.

Teitelbaum, P. & B. A. Campbell. Ingestion patterns in hyperphagic and normal rats. *Journal of Comparative and Physiological Psychology*, 1958, **51**, 135–141.

Teitelbaum, P. & A. M. Epstein. The lateral hypothalamic syndrome: Recovery of feeding and drinking after lateral hypothalamic lesion. *Psychological Review*, 1962, **69**, 74–90.

Tepperman, J., J. R. Brobeck & C. N. H. Long. The effects of hypothalamic hyperphagia and of alterations in feeding habits on the metabolism of the albino rat. *Yale Journal of Biology and Medicine*, 1943, **15**, 855–879.

Tinbergen, N. *The Study of Instinct*. Oxford: Oxford University Press, 1951.

Tompkins, V. H. Stress in aviation. In J. Hambling (Ed.), *The Nature of Stress Disorder*. Springfield, Ill.: Charles C. Thomas, 1959.

Towbin, E. J. Gastric distention as a factor in the satiation of thirst in esophagustomized dogs. *American Journal of Physiology*, 1949, **159**, 533–541.

Towbin, E. J. The role of the gastrointestinal tract in the regulation of water intake. In M. J. Wayner (Ed.), *Thirst: First International Symposium on Thirst in the Regulation of Body Water*. Oxford: Pergamon Press, 1964, pp. 79–94.

Ulrich, R. E. & N. H. Azrin. Reflexive fighting in response to aversive stimulation. *Journal of Experimental Analysis of Behavior*, 1962, **5**, 511–520.

Ulrich, R. E., R. R. Hutchinson & N. H. Azrin. Pain-elicited aggression. *Psychological Record*, 1965, **15**, 111–126.

Utall, W. R. & M. Krisshoff. The response of the somesthetic system to patterned trains of electrical stimuli: An approach to the problem of sensory coding. In D. R. Kenshalo (Ed.), *International Symposium on Skin Senses*. Springfield, Ill.: Charles C. Thomas, 1967.

Vogel, W., S. Raymond & R. S. Lazarus. Intrinsic motivation and psychological stress. *Journal of Abnormal and Social Psychology*, 1959, **58**, 225–233.

von Frey, M. Beitrage zur Sinnes-physiologie der Haut III. *Ber. königl. Sachs. Gesellsch. Wiss. Math–Phys. Kl.*, 1895, **47**, 166.

Watson, J. B. *Psychology from the Standpoint of a Behaviorist*. Philadelphia: Lippincott, 1919.

Watson, J. B. *Behaviorism* (rev. ed.). New York: Norton, 1930.

Watson, J. B. & Rosalie Rayner. Conditional emotional reactions. *Journal of Experimental Psychology*, 1920, **3**, 1–14.

Weddell, G., W. Pallie & E. Palmer. The morphology of peripheral nerve termination in the skin. *Quarterly Journal of Microscopical Science*, 1954, **95**, 483–501.

Weddell, G., E. Palmer & W. Pallie. Nerve endings in mammalian skin. *Biological Reviews of the Cambridge Philosophical Society*, 1955, **30**, 159–195.

Weiner, I. H. & E. Stellar. Salt preference of the rat determined by a single-stimulus method. *Journal of Comparative and Physiological Psychology*, 1951, **44**, 394–401.

Weitzman, E. D., H. Schaumberg & W. Fishbein. Plasma 17-hydroxycorticosteroid levels during sleep in man. Washington, D.C.: APSS, 1965.

Weisner, B. P. & N. M. Sheard. Sex behavior in hypophysectomized male rats. *Nature* (London), 1933, **132**, 641.

White, J. F. The effects of induced muscular tension on heart rate and concept formation. Unpublished doctoral dissertation, Florida State University, 1965.

Wilson, R. S. On behavior pathology. *Psychological Bulletin,* 1963, **60**, 130–146.

Winch, R. F. The relation between loss of parents and progress in courtship. *Journal of Social Phychology,* 1949, **29**, 51–56.

Winslow, C. E. A., L. P. Herrington & A. P. Gagge. Relations between atmospheric condition, physiological reactions and sensations of pleasantness. *American Journal of Hygiene,* 1937, **26**, 103–115.

Wolf, A. V. Osmometric analysis of thirst in man and dog. *American Journal of Physiology,* 1950, **161**, 75–86.

Wolff, C. T., S. B. Friedman, M. A. Hofer & J. W. Mason. Relationship between psychological defenses and mean urinary 17-hydroxycorticosteroid excretion rates: I. A predictive study of parents of fatally ill children. *Psychosomatic Medicine,* 1964, **26**, 576–591.

Wolpe, J. Quantitative relations in the systematic desensitization treatment of phobias. *American Journal of Psychiatry,* 1963, **119**, 1062–1068.

Wood, C. G. The effects of induced muscular tension on learning and recall. Unpublished doctoral dissertation. Florida State University, 1964.

Wood, C. G. & J. E. Hokanson. Effects of induced muscular tension on performance and the inverted U function. *Journal of Personality and Social Psychology,* 1965, **1**, 506–510.

Woodworth, R. S. *Dynamic Psychology.* New York: Columbia University Press, 1918.

Woolsey, C. N. Patterns of localization in sensory and motor areas of the cerebral cortex. In Millbank Memorial Fund, 27th annual Conference, *The Biology of Mental Health and Disease.* New York: Hoeber, 1952, Chap. 14.

Wundt, W. *Outlines of Psychology* (translated by C. H. Judd). Leipzig: W. Engelmann, 1897.

Wyrwicka, W., C. Dobrzecka & R. Tarnecki. On the instrumental conditioned reaction evoked by electrical stimulation of the hypothalamus. *Science,* 1959, **130**, 336–337.

Wyrwicka, W. & C. Dobrzecka. Relationship between feeding and satiation centers of the hypothalamus. *Science,* 1960, **132**, 805–806.

Young, P. T. *Motivation and Emotion. A Survey of the Determinants of Human and Animal Activity.* New York: Wiley, 1961.

Index

Acetylcholine, 45, 60, 112, 159
Adaptation, 103
ADH, *see* Antidiuretic hormone
Adipsia, 61, 62
Adrenal cortex, 18, 31, 36, 75, 77, 126, 154
Adrenaline, *see* Epinephrine
Adrenal medulla, 36, 75, 77, 112, 126, 159
Adrenergic substances, 45, 60, 112, 159
Adrenotrophin, 154
Affectional response, 96
Aggression, 99, 106, 119, 120, 127
Alertness, 22, 113, 123, 151
All-or-none principle, 6
Alpha waves, 14
Ambient temperature, 72
Amygdala, 93, 111, 135, 157
Androgens, 84–86, 94, 138
Androsterone, 84
Anterior hypothalmus, 59, 70, 71, 78–81, 92, 94, 113, 154
Anterior pituitary, 85, 86, 91, 94, 98
Antidiuretic hormone (ADH), 53, 58, 60, 61, 63, 154
Anxiety, 13, 29, 120, 124
Aphagia, 42, 61
Appetite, 48
Arousal, 20–21, 31, 90, 111, 118–119, 154
  history of, 12
  physiology of, 13–21
  and task efficiency, 26–28
Association fibers, 156
Attention, 20, 24–25, 124, 151
Audition, 23, 143
Autonomic nervous system, 16–17, 24, 28, 80, 111, 113, 118–119, 121, 126–127, 154, 157–159
  chemical transmitters, 159
  parasympathetic division, 158
  sympathetic division, 158
Aversive stimulation, 100–129
  behavioral responses, 101–115, 121–125
  physiological responses, 107–117
  stress reactions, 117–129
Avoidance behavior, 101, 103

Basal ganglia, 157
Behaviorism, 5, 130
Blood pressure, 113
Brain stem, 158

Calories, 33, 40, 60, 77
Castration, 84–85
Central intensity monitor, 125
Central nervous system, 147–157
  brain, cerebellum, 151, 152

cerebrum, 155–157
diencephalon, 152–155
limbic system, 157
medulla, 150–151
midbrain, 152
pons, 151
reticular formation, 151–152
spinal cord, 148–149
  afferents, 155
  efferents, 149
Cerebellum, 24, 144, 149, 151–152, 155
Cerebrum, 7, 155–158
Chemical coding, 45, 60
Cholinergic effects, 45, 112, 159
Cingulate gyrus, 135, 157
Cochlear nucleus, 25, 151
Cognition, 119, 122, 129
Cold fibers, 67
Colliculi, 152
Commissural fibers, 156
Conception, 82–83
Conditioned emotional response, 101
Conditioned suppression, 105–106
Conflict, 122
Convection, 73
Corpus callosum, 156
Corpus luteum, 87
Corpus striatum, 152
Cortex, 18, 22, 25, 34, 90, 109, 115, 144, 151, 156
Corticofugal system, 24
Corticopontile fibers, 151
Corticospinal tracts, 149–150
Cranial temperature, 71, 74
Critical periods, 127
Curiosity, 140

Darwinian theory, 3, 130
Delta waves, 16
Diabetes insipidus, 53
Discrimination, 21, 122
Dopa, 31
Dorsal-column tract, 108–109
Dorsal horns, 109–110
Dreams, autonomic correlates, 28
  biochemical processes, 30–31
  deprivation of, 29–30
  EEG, 28
  individual patterns, 28–29
  REM, 28–31
  verbal reports, 28
Drinking, absorption, 50
  central nervous system, 58–63
  deficit, 52–53
  gastrointestinal tract, 53–56
  learning variables, 63
  osmotic pressure, 50–51